Through approachable, warm-hearted letters, Bonnie guides young women to become agents in their lives and relationships. As the author explores relatable anxieties, readers can address the uncertainties they may feel in fully accepting their God-given sexuality.

—Dr. Jennifer Finlayson-Fife
Relationship and sexuality educator

I wish I would have had this book much earlier in my life. The messages that it contains are powerful and desperately needed. Bonnie combines faith, science, and humor beautifully. This book will undoubtedly bless the lives of LDS youth and young adults for years to come.

—Carlie Palmer-Webb
The Christian Sex Educator

I appreciate Bonnie sharing so candidly her perspectives and experiences with sexuality. This book is a must read for adolescents who are also navigating their own maturation process.

—Tammy Hill, LMFT
Professor at BYU's School of Family Life

Sex Educated: Letters from a Latter-day Saint Therapist to Her Younger Self is a fine example of how to delicately and appropriately discuss matters of sexuality with girls and women. By using the approach of writing letters to her younger self as a frame for teaching about sexuality the author presents sexuality in a wonderful tone from a trusted source. She does so

D1603470

with an engaging and gradual discussion of sexual maturity for younger girls and then transitions to a more direct description of sexuality as her letters progress to her older self. In this way the added level of directness does not come across as jarring or inappropriate, rather it is just a natural progression like sexuality development is in life. It is a good model for parents to follow in their attempts to educate children. Additionally, by having consistent discussion across the lifespan this book includes enough detail to be much more useful than the general talk about sexuality many parents are prone to give in their awkward "birds and bees" discussion, yet this additional detail is in no way tawdry or inappropriate. It includes discussing specific body parts and purposes, ways of managing sexual arousal and desire during adolescence and dating relationships, learning to adjust to sexuality during marriage, challenges that may occur during pregnancy and child rearing and aging, and above all the importance of expressing sexuality in a way that honors the needs of women within a spiritual framework. I think this is an invaluable book for both mothers and fathers and daughters.

—Dr. Dean Busby
Director of BYU's School of Family Life

SEX
EDUCATED

BCC
PRESS

BY COMMON CONSENT PRESS is a non-profit publisher dedicated to producing affordable, high-quality books that help define and shape the Latter-day Saint experience. BCC Press publishes books that address all aspects of Mormon life. Our mission includes finding manuscripts that will contribute to the lives of thoughtful Latter-day Saints, mentoring authors and nurturing projects to completion, and distributing important books to the Mormon audience at the lowest possible cost.

SEX
EDUCATED

Letters from a Latter-day Saint
therapist to her younger self

✦ Bonnie Young, LMFT ✦

Edited by Sam Petersen

For information contact
By Common Consent Press
4900 Penrose Dr.
Newburgh, IN 47630

Cover art: Carly White
Cover design: D Christian Harrison
Book design: Andrew Heiss
Editor: Sam Petersen

www.bccpress.org
ISBN-13: 978-1-948218-79-5

10 9 8 7 6 5 4 3 2 1

To my mother, and the mothers that came before her.

To my daughter, and the daughters that will follow.

And to my twelve-year-old self,
and the twelve-year-old girl in all of us.

Contents

Dear Reader   xiii

LETTER 1   Can We Talk? (AGE 10)   1

LETTER 2   Sex is Good (AGE 12)   7

LETTER 3   The Power Pack (AGE 13)   15

LETTER 4   Your Body (AGE 14)   27

LETTER 5   You Can Say No (AGE 15)   33

LETTER 6   Your Sexual Response, Part 1 (AGE 16)   39

LETTER 7   Your Sexual Response, Part 2 (AGE 17)   53

LETTER 8   What Kind of Sex Do You Want? (AGE 18)   59

LETTER 9   Your Unique Sexuality (AGE 20)   69

LETTER 10   Read This Now and
Before Your Honeymoon (AGE 22)   87

LETTER 11   Your Sexual Journey (AGE 26)   95

LETTER 12   Sex Educated (AGE 28)   105

Further Reading and Education   115

Notes   119

A NOTE FROM THE EDITOR

Bonnie and I were newly married when we started this book. We both had just written articles about sex for school, so the topic was fresh on our minds. The clients Bonnie saw in therapy sessions frequently brought up sexual issues, plus we had our fair share of issues, too. Sex was clearly the source of a lot of hurt and frustration. We felt like if people—especially Latter-day Saints—were better educated about sex then it wouldn't be such a struggle for them. It dawned on us one day that we were in a position to perhaps relieve some suffering at a grander scale by producing a book, this book. And thus began a long journey to publish the pages now in front of you.

Sex Educated is a collection of reflective essays about sex and sexuality in letter format addressed to Bonnie's younger self at different ages. She combines personal stories, anecdotes from her therapy clients, Latter-day Saint scriptures, and research-backed theories to educate the reader about sex- and sexuality-related topics. The letters explore God's perspective on sex, how sex works, consent, sex and the media, the effect of body image on sex, the purposes of sex, women and sexuality, and other topics. But note that this book is not meant to answer all questions about sex—it doesn't address non-heterosexual themes, masturbation, toys, lubricants, lingerie, STIs, and many other sex-related topics. You can find a "recommended readings" section near the back of the book with suggestions of other sources for a deeper and broader study of sex and sexuality.

Sex is a tricky theme to write about within the Latter-day Saint community, because we consider it to be very sacred. Bonnie and I took great care to make this book a reverent, respectful, and faith-promoting resource. (Although not written for children, rest assured there is nothing in this book that would hurt a child if they happened upon it.) Reverence, respect, and faith, however, can and should exist together with accurate descriptions of anatomy and physiology, appreciation for one's God-given sexual capacity, and the denunciation of unhealthy perspectives and attitudes. Oh, and some humor here and there. Expect all of that within these pages.

Lastly, I want to acknowledge that this book is written by a woman to a woman. And I expect more women will read it than men. But I will attest that any man who reads these pages will become a better friend to all women, a stronger father to his daughters, and a more empathetic lover to his wife. I've become all of these because of Bonnie's book. So, women, don't hesitate to share this with the men in your life. And men, please don't walk away just because it's written to women.

I hope you'll let *Sex Educated* play a role in your journey to find greater peace.

God bless you on that journey.

Sam Petersen

Dear Reader,

The letters that follow contain what I wish I could tell my younger self about sex in all of her pubescent, adolescent, and young adult glory. They are in the order I would have sent them, starting around age ten and finishing in my early adult life. And while these letters are addressed to my younger self, they are mostly intended for you, dear reader.

Perhaps you were a bit like me when you were younger. Perhaps, like me, you've felt unsure or frustrated with your sexuality. Maybe, like me, you've experienced shame about your sexuality. And maybe you need education and healing in order to fully embrace and love the sexual side of you. I wrote these letters to counter shame and promote deeper understanding so that you can take healing steps toward a better relationship with your body, your emotions, your partner, your children, and even with God.

A lot of people avoid talking about sex because it's uncomfortable, and a lot of people avoid it because it's so special. Both of these are mistakes. I hope to correct some of the unintended consequences of that silence in these pages.

I believe you can find truth and healing in these letters. Each time I felt hesitant to share so much about my story while writing, I reminded myself that I am sharing these stories to help women like me. Healing occurs in many ways. I have found incredible healing in knowing that I'm not alone in my experiences.

You should know that, despite the fact that the first few letters of this book address a child, this is not a children's book. I've written it for a mature reader—think older teenagers to grandmothers—who can reflect on their own sexual journey, including how they felt about their sexuality when they were younger and what the future might hold for them. That said, this book can have a powerful effect on how you approach teaching the next generation. Your increased understanding of and comfort with your own sexuality will expand your ability to pass down healthy truths about sex and sexuality to your children (or future children, or any young person within your sphere of influence).

Let me be clear to the parents or aspiring parents reading this right now. More than any book, *you* are the greatest tool in educating your children about sex. Sex education resources written for kids can be helpful, don't get me wrong. (See the further readings section at the end of the book for a great book on teaching kids about sex.) And of course the tone and content of my letters in this book can serve as a model of how to talk to your kids about sex at different ages. But the most important thing that you can do in educating your children about sexuality is to work on your relationship with sex. How you feel about sex, your body, showing affection, feeling pleasure, letting go, being loved, accepting yourself and your partner—these are the things that will speak the loudest as you educate your children about sex. So, let this book be a tool for you to get sex educated—a healthier sex education for your children will follow naturally. (This goes for both women and men teaching both sons and daughters—children should learn from both parents, not just the parent of the same sex.)

As you read these letters, be sure to take some time to reflect. Pray for courage. Ponder on the aspects of your sexual life you would like to change. Seek healing and growth through learning, practice, and self-compassion. If necessary, seek out professional help.

I hope that these letters will provide you with hope, power, and love for yourself and for Heavenly Parents who created you.

Warmly,
Bonnie

Can We Talk?

AGE 10

Dear Bonnie,

It's me (you) in the future. Did you know that you grow up to be a therapist, and that you frequently help people with sexual problems? Does that give you a pit in your stomach? Please don't stop reading these letters when you see that I'm writing about sex.

I know, that word makes you feel weird. It has since you were really young. Like the time a few years ago when your family was having a gospel lesson about chastity and you hid under your ballerina blanket on the brown couch in the family room and cried because you were so uncomfortable. That's part of the reason these letters are so important to read. I know what you're feeling right now, and I know what you'll go through in the years to come. I want to help you get to the point where you're not intimidated by the topic of sex. Feeling confident about sex, especially your own sexuality, will bring more peace to your life. These letters will help you get there, even though they make you uncomfortable right now.

If it makes you feel any better, most people are just as uncomfortable talking about sex as you are, Bonnie. How do I know? It's my job. I've talked to hundreds, maybe thousands of people about sex, and I can tell you, you're not alone.

Even though it's uncomfortable to talk about, you're also curious about it right now. This is a good thing. But if you're not properly educated, you'll piece together a confusing and incomplete picture of sex that will take a lot of effort to fix later. (And it does, by the way. Lots of effort.) I want to help you learn truth about sex.

You might feel hesitant, though, to learn about sex. You might think learning about sex is sinful. A lot of young people think that if they avoid the subject of sex, even in educational contexts, their ignorance will give them more power to remain chaste. A lot of adults think that if young people are educated about sex, they'll take that knowledge and go experiment and get into trouble. (Just so you know, the opposite is true in both of these cases.[1]) You could even be afraid at the feelings you get when you read about or discuss sex in safe, appropriate settings.

But here's the thing, whether you are intentional about it or not, every day you are exposed to information that creates some version of your sex education. It's unavoidable. So, Bonnie, you get to choose. Do you want lunch-room conversations at your school, lyrics from pop songs, and that sexy scene in a movie to teach you about sex? Or, would you rather be taught truths about sex from someone who loves you and wants you to be happy?

Even though you've been told a lot of half-truths about sex, and from that stuff you've figured that sex is dirty and ungodly, I need you to know that it actually isn't. I know this is one of the first times you've heard someone say sex isn't bad. Let me explain a little more.

A lot of the things that you've heard about sex (how the world often talks about sex) are not helpful because they're crude or false. So in a way you're right, that version of sex doesn't feel good. And that's not how God wants you to feel or talk about sex. But the version of sex that is part of the plan of salvation—and the fact that you are a sexual being and your body is sexual and you will someday have a sexual relationship with your spouse—that is good. It is *so* good. It is not naughty.

These letters will teach you God's version of sex. Over the next eighteen years, the letters that I'll send will teach you about your sexuality, the purposes of sex, and the role sex will play throughout your life. As you read these letters, you will come to understand the multi-dimensional nature of sex. What I mean by that is that sex isn't just a physical experience, but also is an emotional, relational, and creational experience.

Bonnie, I hope that as you read these letters, you'll feel respect for your body. I hope that you can replace the hiding-under-the-ballerina-blanket anxiety with confidence and power. As you learn about your sexuality, I hope that you will feel proud to be you, and that you will gain a greater respect for the person you were born to be. I hope that you'll be able to spot lies about sex that surround you and replace them with truths. I also hope you'll feel more comfortable discussing sex with trustworthy people in your life—espescially your future husband. He's awesome, by the way.

You're a lovely young lady, Bonnie.

Love,

Me

Sex is Good

AGE 12

Dear Bonnie,

By now you've heard and read things like "the natural man is an enemy to God" (Mosiah 3:19). Or that we have to "bridle our passions" (Alma 38:12), and that there is no sin that is greater than sexual sin besides murder and denying the Holy Ghost (Alma 39:5). From these and other scriptures and lessons, you've come to the conclusion that your sexual nature must be bad.

You're not alone. A lot of religious people believe sexual feelings are "Satan's pathway" to lead us to sin.[1] Some people see sex and sexual feelings as evil but necessary for bringing babies into the world. How can something that is thought to be so bad also be good?

Let me share one of my favorite quotes from Parley P. Pratt, one of the first latter-day apostles, to help frame what I believe God thinks of sex.

> Some persons have supposed that our natural affections [i.e., sexual natures] were the results of a fallen and corrupt nature, and that they are 'carnal, sensual, and devilish,' and therefore ought to be resisted, subdued, or overcome as so many evils which prevent our perfection, or progress in the spiritual life. In short, that they should be greatly subdued in this world, and in the world to come entirely done away. . . . So far from this being the case, our natural affections are planted in us by the Spirit of God, for a wise purpose; and they are the very main-springs of life and happiness—they are the cement of all virtuous and heavenly society—they are the essence of charity, or love.[2]

I think what Parley is saying here responds to your worries, and I think he would agree that the version of sex you're exposed to in the media and from friends is not what God wants.

But let me make a distinction here. Sex itself isn't "carnal, sensual, and devilish." Rather, it's the obsessive fixation on the body as an object. It's the giving of the self without being able to truly give the whole self. It's the selfishness, it's the betrayal, it's the focus on "me" without care or concern for "you." It's the manipulation and power plays. Bonnie, *those* are the things that are carnal, sensual, and devilish.

So if this is what sex is, then yes, sex ought to be "resisted, subdued, [and] overcome." This type of sex is sin.

But the sex that Parley is referring to—godly sex—is different. Godly sex combines our potential for physical pleasure with our natural desire to completely connect with and belong to a committed partner. Godly sex includes eroticism and creativity (whose pinnacle is procreation) and wholehearted sharing of oneself. Sex, in this way, is the "essence of charity," because it inclines spouses to share themselves more completely, consecrate their devotion, and build a more enduring relationship. Sex as a bonding, nurturing, loving, and safe refuge for spouses can act as "the cement of all virtuous and heavenly society."[3]

What about those scriptures that I mentioned

earlier that seem to contradict what Parley is saying? Let me reassure you the "natural man" referred to by King Benjamin isn't synonymous with "man's sexual nature" but rather refers to our inclination to be prideful and self-centered.[4] While it is a good thing to have sexual discipline, I don't think that was the *only* thing Alma was referring to when he told his son Shiblon to "bridle his passions." When read in context, "bridling passions" can be interpreted as being temperate, gentle, and principled, and could refer to Shiblon's youthful zeal as well as his sexuality. And finally, the idea that sexual sin is the "third worst" offense (only after shedding innocent blood and denying the Holy Ghost) may be a misreading of Alma 39.[5] I believe that Alma was not only referring to the sin of lusting after others but also to the sins of "boasting in his own wisdom" (being prideful) and "forsaking the ministry" (abandoning responsibility) when he told Corianton that "*these things* [emphasis added] are an abomination in the sight of the Lord." These scriptures warn us of using our sexuality in prideful and lustful ways. Doing this is sin. But let me say this again: It is the pride, lust, and disregard for God's commandments that makes sex sinful in these situations. Sex in and of itself is not sinful.

In fact, there are many places in the scriptures that talk about the goodness of sex. One of the very first commandments that God gave to Eve and Adam was to have sex.[6] He wanted them to use their sexual desires and natures to create new life between them and from them. In the New Testament, Jesus taught that a man should "cleave to his wife" (cleaving means to stick to) and that spouses should be "one flesh."[7] In other words, Christ commands all married couples to become one flesh through sex.[8]

Multiple latter-day leaders have echoed these words. In "The Family: A Proclamation to the World," the First Presidency and Twelve Apostles declared that, "The means by which mortal life is created [is] divinely appointed." I'm not sure if I need to clarify this or not, but the "means by which mortal life is created" is sexual union between woman and man.

Dr. Wendy Watson Nelson, a retired professor of family therapy, as well as the wife of President Russell M. Nelson, taught that sex is God-ordained, an important part of marital love, that "the Lord wants a husband and wife to partake of the wonders and joys of marital intimacy," and that sex "is commanded and commended by Him because it draws a husband and wife closer together and closer to the Lord!"[9]

Similarly, Spencer W. Kimball taught that the Bible celebrates sexual union between spouses, "presenting it as God-created, God-ordained, [and] God-blessed."[10] Bonnie, God created humans to be sexual! It's part of his plan. It is an essential part of our nature.

Our sexual power is the key to fully participating in the plan of salvation.[11] We are created in the image of our Heavenly Parents. All of our parts are a reflection of all of Their parts, including our sexual parts and potentials. The sexual nature and potential we are born with is good and godly. Just like any other part of mortality, our sexual natures require refining.[12] I'll talk more about that refining in other letters.

"So," you might say, "This is all fine for a decade from now when I'm married and this is relevant, but what does it have to do with right now?"

The answer is this: What you are learning about

sex at this stage of your life will have a lot to do with how you feel about sex in the future, as well as how you feel about yourself now. How you feel about sex has incredible impact on the sexual relationship you form with your partner once you are married. Also, how you respond to your sexual feelings now has the power to create patterns of behavior that will continue during marriage.

If you find that you respond to your feelings with shame, fear, or disgust, those feelings may follow you into adulthood and emerge in your marriage. And at the same time, responding to your feelings with entitlement now ("I want it, so I'm going to do it," or "I am a girl / boy, and this is how girls / boys are"), may also carry into your marriage.

Learning how to respond to your sexual feelings both before and during marriage is a process, and you will probably make mistakes, because you are human. Development requires resistance, falling short, and trying again. Bonnie, do you think you can find a way to respond to your sexual feelings, thoughts, and desires in a way that is affirming and yet disciplined? Is there a way to acknowledge that your sexuality is good and godly and also respond

with healthy boundaries around your sexual behavior? When you do make mistakes, do you think
that you can repent in a way that recognizes that
you are good, and your sexual desires are good, and
that the mistake came in the timing or context? I'd
love to know your thoughts.

My dearest Bonnie, be kind to yourself.

Love,

Me

The Power Pack

AGE 13

Dear Bonnie,

You might melt into whatever you're sitting in as you read this. So, take a deep breath. I'm here with you, holding your hand. Giggling. And crying. And giggling some more.

I know about the Power Pack.

I know how quiet you want to be about your body changing. Like, really quiet. Like, an I'm-going-to-keep-the-fact-that-I-am-going-through-puberty-a-total-secret kind of quiet.

But you actually tell the story about your Power Pack to a group of friends when you're seventeen at Flying Pie Pizzeria. You've never laughed so hard in your life. You and your friends were all in tears, laughing so hard you almost couldn't get the words of the story out. It was like a confession that hurt so bad that all you could do was laugh.

Even if it's agony now, you'll laugh about it . . . eventually. And maybe as you read it from my perspective now, you'll see some humor in it.

Bonnie, you got your first period about when most girls do. It was the summer after sixth grade. It was mid-day and sunny outside. You went to the bathroom and your heart dropped when you saw blood on your underwear. It had come. Too embarrassed to ask your family for tips or pointers, you decided to go it alone. You remembered that you had seen some of your sisters' pads and tampons in the bathroom cabinet. You started with a tampon and almost fainted trying to insert it (why did your sisters buy tampons with no applicators?). That's when you figured pads were the easiest way to go. Just a couple rips (very loud rips—you know the type) and a slap and you had a full-on blood diaper in your panties. Simple.

Except for the fact that "ripping open this pad" is as loud as opening a bag of chips in a quiet room. And it was already embarrassing that you had a period *and* that you couldn't put in a tampon without fainting. (You might have been less embarrassed had you known that one of your friends mistook her anus for her vagina and walked around all day with a tampon literally up her butt.) Still, you didn't want anyone knowing that (1) you were on your period, and (2) you were using grandma pads. So you invented the "Power Pack." Yes, it's a proper noun now ;).

You secretly named it a few years later, because it helps to explain your brilliant invention. Let me remind you that during this stage of life, you were really into layers. We're talking two layers minimum. Undershirt, top shirt, vest. Or, under-undershirt, undershirt, top shirt, sweatshirt. The goal was to hide as much of your body as possible. The result was lots of stinky laundry and hard-to-repair social consequences.

But back to the Power Pack. Here was your solution to the noisy pad wrapper problem:

Before school, you'd sneak into the upstairs bathroom closet and take out three to four jumbo pads. You'd hide them under your arm, run down the hallway to your bedroom, and then shut the door. Carefully, you'd unwrap and unstick each pad from the package and place it on your first shirt layer. You would repeat this three to four times until you had all of the potential pads stuck to your undershirt. You'd then pop on your second shirt over the pad-laden undershirt, and then cover it all up with your trusty vest, and voila! You were ready for the day!

Nobody would suspect anything! Take a purse into the bathroom? No thank you! You were free and easy, and nobody was going to hear anything through those bathroom stalls. When you needed to change pads, you'd unsuspiciously walk into the bathroom, carefully peel the used pad off of your cotton undies, and place it in the waste bin. (Those things creak, so you had to be really careful about that part.) Then you'd ever-so-slowly peel a new pad off the Power Pack, and stick it in your undies. Mission accomplished.

Bonnie, first off, this is truly brilliant. I love your creativity and stealth. You might think it's crazy that you share this story with anyone, but the more you share it the more stories like it you hear from other people (e.g., tampon up the butt). It seems like most adolescent girls and boys have their own version of some ultra embarrassing puberty-related event. But these stories also break my heart a little bit.

One reason we hide things—whether it be keeping secrets or wearing layers to hide our bodies—is because we feel shame about them. We feel shame when we feel like there is something wrong with us. We feel shame when we are afraid of letting others know the truth about us. Shame loves keeping secrets.

Shame is different from guilt. You feel guilt when you've done something wrong, and guilt helps you know that you can change. Guilt tells you there is something wrong with something you've done, but shame tells you that there is something wrong with *you*. I can tell that you feel shame about your body and becoming a woman. You feel like it is *wrong* to develop breasts, grow pubic hair, or to start menstruating. I want to help you identify why you think it's wrong, change your attitudes about yourself, and help you understand that while this development is awkward, it is actually an opportunity to mature into a woman who is confident, graceful in complexity, and powerful.

I think one of the reasons you're overcome by shame and hide yourself in extreme, albeit clever ways is that you've become aware of how the world objectifies women's bodies and you desperately don't want that to happen to you. One of your biggest fears right now is that as you develop sexually, that your sexuality is *all* that others will begin to see in you. It isn't difficult to understand why you feel this way. The world often first portrays women as sexual objects; women's bodies are constantly on display and are the focus of constant evaluation. You notice boys at school talking about girls who are developing breasts earlier than most. You notice the camera angles in just about any visual media slowly scanning the woman's body, stopping at her curves, before getting to her face. You don't want to be looked at as if you are just your breasts, or curvy hips. You want to be seen as the whole person you are—emotions, ideas, as well as your appearance.

Another source of the shame you feel about your body is the way you've often been taught about modesty and the importance of covering up your body. Being taught about modesty isn't bad, but some of the messages you've received have missed the mark.[1] Even before your body began to change, you were told that it was wrong to show your shoulders, thighs, or cleavage (which took a while to come around . . . and let's be honest, you still don't have much . . . but I digress). You were told that if you wore something too tight or too low or too high or that shifted too much when you moved, you would become "walking pornography" to young men who were trying to stay morally clean, or at the very least that you would cause them to have bad thoughts. For someone like you who takes her religion very seriously and wants to be strictly obedient, these messages aren't easy to brush off or compartmentalize. These teachings about modesty often created fear of your body and its potential for causing sin in someone else.

Bonnie, this fear is wrong. Yes, you have the responsibility to treat your body in a way that reflects respect towards yourself and your Heavenly Parents. But how others react to your body isn't your responsibility. Let me point out that *nowhere* in the scriptures does Christ tell women to cover up their bodies. He doesn't blame women for creating impure thoughts in the men around them. There are, however, multiple places where Jesus condemns objectifying and lusting after others. I like how Christian writer Rachel Held Evans said it: "Notice Jesus doesn't say, 'everyone who looks at a woman with lust has already committed adultery with her in his heart, so ladies, be sure to dress more modestly.' Instead he says to the men, 'if your right eye causes you to sin, tear it out and throw it away!'"[2] Jesus doesn't want us to look at anyone with lustful intent or to see them as objects. If we do, it's *our* responsibility, not theirs.[3] More than women covering themselves, Christ wants all people to get their hearts in the right place.

There is something I want you to never forget about sexual objectification and abuse. The responsibility of sexual objectification or abuse lies squarely on the shoulders of the objectifier and the abuser. Let me say it again: When someone chooses to see you or treat you as an object rather than a beloved daughter of God, this is their fault, never yours. Jesus backs me up on this.

It's also your responsibility to make sure that you aren't objectifying yourself or others. When we dress and groom ourselves, we can do it in a way that reflects and respects the truth that we are not just an object to be observed, but rather a whole being with divine potential and purpose. Likewise, each person you see is a daughter or son of Heavenly Parents, created in Their image, with talents, struggles, and dreams. While how we choose to present ourselves can be a reflection of how we feel about ourselves, our appearance is not a true or complete reflection of who we are.

Bonnie, I can also sense that you think you can't be excited or happy about the changes that are happening to you (turning into a woman). You feel that's wrong, because you should always be modest.

Some of your friends at your middle school made up a chant about their changing bodies. As they would march in a circle, they'd exclaim, "We must! We must! We must increase our bust!" You feel confused by the fact that these girls can talk so comfortably about their bodies, and that they even want their bodies to change. You feel a tinge of jealousy that they escaped the shame that you feel enveloped in. Then you push the shame even deeper and conclude that they were being irreverent about their bodies. You tell yourself that these feelings aren't about your own insecurity with your body, they are about these girls parading their bodies in an unrighteous manner.

Bonnie, it's okay that they sing that song. It's okay that you have periods. It's okay that they are, and you are, maturing. And it's okay that you are sexual.

The world sends messages to you that are conflicting and confusing. When you have so much information bombarding you, it's hard to discern what is true. It's hard to be told that you're supposed to be modest and not mix that message up with the idea that your natural figure is sinful, or causes others to sin. It's hard to be told that your body is good and godly, but then be bombarded with images of sexualized women's bodies. It's confusing to be told that becoming capable of procreation is part of our Heavenly Parents' plan but then also be told that sex is dirty.

It will get clearer as you get older. I hope these letters will help.

Bonnie, your body was created in the image of your Heavenly Mother. Each part of you was created to reflect Her. This means *every* part, including your breasts, hips, vulva, and vagina. She is good and whole and holy. As you go through puberty and become a woman, you are developing in a way to become even more like Her. It will take practice and discipline to use your body in the way that She does. Your sexual parts and capacities are a reflection of Hers. Your body is not bad or dirty. Your shape is not bad or dirty. Your sexual feelings and thoughts are not bad or dirty.

Before Satan introduced his twisted ideas to Eve and Adam in the Garden of Eden, they weren't ashamed of their bodies. It was only Satan who told them to hide themselves. I think in the same way that Satan told lies to our first parents, he tells us lots of lies about our bodies and our sexual natures. Don't believe him.

When woman and man were created in the garden of Eden, God made sure that we knew that He called them "good."

You are good, Bonnie.

Love,
Me

Your Body

AGE 14

Dear Bonnie,

You are fourteen now, and you still feel uncomfortable with your changing body. Nobody tells you this, but your body will continue changing—getting rounder then smaller, stronger then softer—for a long time.

Right now, you feel like your body is not good enough. It's not muscular enough, skinny enough, tall enough, tan enough, and the list goes on. You're very hard on yourself for the parts you feel aren't acceptable, and you try to hide these. You do the shorts-over-swimsuits and change-in-bathroom-stalls and wear-loose-clothing things not just because you believe that these are "modest," but because you feel your body isn't "good enough" to not do these things.

You also worry a lot about being pretty. Someone made a comment about "butt-chins" once and it has made you self-conscious about your cleft chin ever since. Unfortunately, you inherited the "adolescent acne" gene from your parents and it got pretty bad this year—so bad that you and your best friend decided to name the constellations that your pimples created on your face. A few months ago, a popular boy at school told you that you had a witch nose. These experiences, among others, have made you feel like others are constantly evaluating your looks and your body. You feel enormous stress every morning as you get dressed and do your hair and makeup.

You have many friends who seem to have perfect bodies and faces, and it's hard to not compare yourself. These comparisons and "not good enoughs" influence your day-to-day feelings about yourself and your worth.

Starting at a very young age, you absorbed the message that you should be dissatisfied with your body. You heard it from the women around you as they talked about how much weight they "needed" to lose and the diets they'd start on Monday. You picked up and internalized things like "counting calories" and "watching your figure."

Do you remember standing in front of the TV in the family room and trying on hand me-downs from a family friend? Do you remember not being able to fit into a particular pair of those pants? You made a mental plan to lose weight so that you would be able to fit into them. You were in the fifth grade.

Here's the thing, Bonnie. Your body exists to enable you to experience the joys of mortality, not just to be looked at. I like how Lexie and Lindsay Kite put it in their book *More Than a Body*: "Your body is an instrument, not an ornament."[1] Your body is good because God created it, not because of how much it weighs or how it looks. You don't get more worth when you are skinnier or more toned. You are fed so many lies about how your body gives you more or less worth. It takes you a while to recognize these lies. In fact, it takes some painful experiences that force you to wake up to these lies.

When you return home from your mission, you feel intense pressure to have your body look a certain way. I'm not sure why it happened after your mission, but it might have had something to do with your "six months to sexy" exercise regimen at the end of your mission, or being in the dating scene and being surrounded by a lot of beautiful and successful people. During this period, you go to extremes to control what you eat and you feel intense guilt when you don't go on your daily five-mile run. You feel obsessed with food and think about it constantly. You view being hungry as a good thing, and the feelings of hunger as something to be proud of or a sign of self-discipline. You feel guilty when you eat normal amounts of food and absolutely ashamed when you eat more than you need to. You generally feel sad around this time, because you constantly feel like you're not good enough.

The most eye-opening experience to your relationship with your body happens during your first pregnancy. (Yes! You get pregnant, and have a beautiful baby. I'm sorry to break it to you, but your pregnancies are *absolutely* miserable. Worth it, of course, but miserable.) You end up losing about fifteen pounds during the first trimester of your first pregnancy, taking you to a weight that you hadn't been at since middle school. You can't keep anything down . . . and I mean anything—not even Jolly

Ranchers. You spend hours—not exaggerating—everyday in the bathroom vomiting.

And you know what else happens during this period of intense sickness and weight loss? You get more praise for your body than ever before. People ask you what you've been doing. You don't tell them the truth, because it is still early enough in your pregnancy that you and your husband don't feel confident sharing the news. But you do notice the irony of the situation: that the time when you receive the most praise for your body is also one of the sickest and unhealthiest times of your life.

You realize that in order to get this kind of attention for your body, you would *literally have to starve yourself*. Something clicks inside you at this time, and you wish you would have known this when you were younger. You start rebelling against messages about an ideal size or shape. You begin recognizing how much of a double standard exists for men's and women's bodies, and this fuels your fire. You feel empowered against those messages. This is good.

My hope for you, Bonnie, is that you can come to love and honor the body that you've been given by Heavenly Parents. I hope you can learn to see yourself not as an object to be observed, but as a complete person with unique talents and potential. Knowing that your body is good and divine, no matter what it looks like, will be a necessary foundation to you as you move forward, especially as your body goes through the many changes that come with childbearing and beyond. The different seasons of your life will necessarily call for different sizes and shapes of your body. Each size and shape is valuable and is evidence of your journey. I like to think of the stretch marks that you gain on your thighs, waist, and breasts as tiger stripes—fleshy tapestries attesting to the fierce and full life you have lived.

When you are feeling insecure or anxious about your appearance, please come back and read this letter.

Love,
Me.

You Can Say No

AGE 15

Dear Bonnie,

You don't need to use your body in ways you don't want to. And you should never make others use their bodies in ways they don't want to, either.

Let me say this another way. If your partner wants to be physical with you in a way that makes you uncomfortable or that feels incongruent in the relationship, tell him, "No!" If you and a partner have decided on certain boundaries, or if your partner has voiced boundaries that he doesn't want to cross, it is wrong to push each other beyond that limit.

Bonnie, you have every right in the world to make things awkward or uncomfortable for another person if they are violating your boundaries. If you don't want to hold hands with him, don't! If you feel strange about kissing him, don't! If you don't want to be touched in a certain place, slap his hand away! Say, "No!" Get out of there. You have the right to stand up for yourself. Nobody has the right to do anything physically to you that you don't want. Period.

It's also very important to know that sometimes you may not be able to prevent unwanted touch or advances. This does not mean that they are your fault. When people are put into a situation where their expectations are wildly disrupted by reality, most respond with shock and are unable to make decisions like they would in normal life. The blame of the action is not to be assigned to them. Who is responsible, then?

Let me answer that question with a story.

During college, a dear friend of mine was invited to hang out by a male friend. They had spent time together before, but she never felt or sensed any romantic interest for or from him. In fact, he had been dating someone else.

She arrived at his house and he excitedly asked her if he could show her something. She agreed, happy to do something spontaneous and creative. They began walking towards campus, entered one of the buildings, and snuck into a large, empty auditorium. My friend thought that they would climb up to the roof or something else harmlessly rebellious.

Instead, he led her behind the curtains on the stage, pulled her close, and began kissing her. She was shocked. Stunned, thoughts began racing through her head. "Why is he doing this?" "What do I do?" "I do not want to be here!" This was the last thing that she expected. But she found herself unable to say, "Stop!" So he continued.

I ask again: Who is responsible for what happened? *He is*. The responsibility of sexual misconduct lies squarely on the shoulders of the perpetrator. And, as Elder Holland reminds us, ". . . for that imposed uncleanliness a man *will pay* [emphasis added], as surely as the sun sets and rivers run to the sea."[1]

Now, while it may seem obvious that you shouldn't do what that idiot did, there are many more subtle things that you need to be aware of when you are navigating romantic relationships. These are red flags that indicate boundaries could be getting violated in a relationship.

- Does a partner push you to give consent

for something that you would rather not
do physically?

- Do you have to convince yourself to do
  something physically that you would rather not participate in?
- Do you feel conflicted about certain physical acts in a relationship?
- Do you feel like you have to do certain
  physical things in a relationship in order to
  keep a partner interested?
- Are you afraid that if you don't do something physically in a relationship that your
  partner will become upset? Do you participate to keep him from becoming angry or
  emotionally disturbed?
- Is the level of physical affection in your
  relationship incongruent with how both of
  you feel about each other?

If the answer to any of these questions was "yes"
or even "a little bit," that is a sign that this could be
an unhealthy (even abusive) relationship. My sug-
gestion to you is to talk about these things with
someone that you trust, and someone who is on

your side. If someone minimizes these concerns or tells you that it is alright to do more than you want to physically, they are not on your side. Surround yourself with people who can support you and give you the courage you need in order to either break off the relationship or to confront these issues with your partner.

You are in charge of you. Nobody else has the right to push you further than you want to go physically, at *any* point in a relationship—including your husband in marriage. Learn to recognize manipulation from others, and never manipulate others, either.

This is serious stuff, Bonnie.

Love,

Me

Your Sexual Response
Part 1

AGE 16

Dear Bonnie,

I want to talk about sex in detail. You've pieced together an *interesting* definition of sex over the years. You've connected some dots—the dots you've gleaned from conversations from friends, a sex-ed lesson at school you tried to tune out, chastity lessons, well-meaning leaders trying to describe masturbation or foreplay without actually using any understandable words, and some weird stuff you came across on the internet, to name a few. So you know that sex requires being naked and using private parts, and something about men and women "fitting together." But if someone asked you about sex, you could not confidently explain it to them.

In an ideal situation, you would have learned about this in age-appropriate doses during your childhood and adolescence. Your parents did the best they knew how, and you get to do the best you know how when you teach your kids. But right now, just know that you're not alone in your partial understanding of sex. Most of your peers have grown up just like you have, and even those who seem to know what's going on probably don't. Remember, that's why I'm writing these letters—to give you a whole, truthful understanding of sex.

Please note that I didn't say, "I'm going to explain how sex works" or, "here's a step-by-step recipe for how people have sex." I've noticed that when people focus on or only teach the mechanics of sex, it leads to some discouraging patterns. One of these is that people may believe that there is only *one* way or a *correct* way to have sex. That's wrong because sex will be different for every couple. It's dangerous, too, because what the world has taught is "the correct way" has historically emphasized men's experiences more than women's.

Sex will also change as you go throughout different stages of your life. (I'll spend more time on both of these very important topics in future letters.) Another danger of focusing too much on the mechanics of sex is that it puts undue emphasis on the physical elements of sex and leaves out the spiritual and emotional aspects.[1] So keep this in mind as you read these letters.

At this point, you might be wondering, "Why do I need to understand these details now? Why can't I just wait until I'm ready to have sex to learn about it?" I can sense you feeling guilty for wanting to read on, or to get more information. You might even feel like you're doing something wrong.

Please, please don't feel this way.

Bonnie, it's essential to know these details. Understanding your own body and arousal patterns can empower you—whether that is in keeping commitments about sexual behavior to yourself or someday understanding yourself in a sexual relationship with your husband. It will increase the respect you have for your body and make you a more confident, compassionate, and respectful partner. And like I mentioned in earlier letters, knowing the truth about sex can help you discern messages in the media and create healthy expectations for your future. This can make the portrayals of sex in the media less powerful—and you'll be able to know what is real and what is a lie.

So, *please* keep reading, even if it feels uncomfortable. I promise it's okay to learn about this.

Let me start first by acknowledging that what most people refer to as sex actually refers to sexual intercourse. (You also might hear it called penetration, coitus, or copulation.) Sexual intercourse is when a man's penis enters a woman's vagina, and, after he experiences sufficient stimulation (through thrusting the penis within the vagina), he ejaculates semen. This is how babies are made. While this is a common understanding of what sex is, it's important to understand that *sex encompasses so, so much more than penis-vagina union, ejaculation, and baby-making.* (Did you notice that the definition of intercourse didn't focus very much on women? Yeah . . . we're definitely going to talk more about this later.) Sex doesn't have to include intercourse to be called sex. Sex doesn't have to be procreative to be called sex. Non-penetrative sex is just as valid as penetrative sex, and it's normally *much more* satisfying for both partners when sex includes *much more* than intercourse.

I want to introduce you to a concept called the "sexual response." It's based on the work of multiple researchers who have studied how people experience sex.[2] It's not comprehensive, but it will help you get a basic idea of the general patterns of sex. I'm going to talk about three parts of the sexual response: arousal, orgasm, and resolution. In this letter, I'm going to talk about the first stage. I'll cover the last two in my next letter.

Our sexual response starts with arousal (also referred to as "excitement" or "getting turned on"). This stage may begin as a couple shares intimate touch (holding hands, hugging, cuddling, kissing, caressing, etc.), but it can also happen simply in the anticipation or imagination of these things. When and how arousal happens really just depends on the person and the situation you are in.

Something to keep in mind is that the arousal stage of the sexual response doesn't just occur when you're intending to have sex. In fact, any couple, committed to abstinence or not, married or not, will experience arousal as they are affectionate together. Bonnie, get to know the content of this letter well so that you can recognize when you're in a situation that's going to lead you away from your goal of waiting until marriage to become sexually active. Ignorance about this stage can lead to unexpected outcomes. Let me share a quick story about this.

I worked with a female client who was engaged to a nice fellow and together they had the goal of abstinence until they were married. They really enjoyed making out and spent quite a bit of time engaging in this . . . pastime. One day she came to our session perplexed and told me that although their goal hadn't changed, they had both been completely clothed, and neither of their hands had been wandering to each other's private parts, she had an orgasm as they were making out. "How did this happen? Why did this happen?" she asked me. She had assumed that as long as they were clothed, weren't touching each other inappropriately, and his penis did not enter her vagina (intercourse), she wouldn't have an orgasm.

Her shock revealed many misconceptions about

sex that she possessed, not only about her patterns of arousal, but about orgasm as well (most women don't experience orgasm through intercourse only, but I'm getting ahead of myself!). We spent the next session talking about signs that her body was giving her that she was becoming more and more aroused.

Bonnie, because I want you to be happy and have healthy relationships with the boys you date, I recommend being really purposeful about the amount of physical affection you show each other. Your ability to choose your sexual boundaries right now is much greater than it will be when you've been kissing your man for a long time. This is because as your level of arousal increases, your desire to continue usually increases with it. (This is natural, because arousal usually feels good!) So if you have a goal to *not* experience orgasm (or to not have penetrative sex, get pregnant, etc.) premaritally, then figure out your personal boundaries (i.e., where *you* should stop, what *you* should avoid), and choose to avoid the spot in your arousal trajectory that would make it harder to live up to your commitment to yourself. While you always have the option to stop at any point with your partner (many people stop themselves pre-orgasm or at other points of arousal), you will do yourself a favor by making these decisions now when your judgment is clearer and you are less vulnerable to doing something that you actually don't want.

So decide now, share your goals with your honey, and stick to it. And know that there will be lots of time to explore and develop those feelings of arousal once you are in the commited context that you desire for the fullest expression of your sexuality. Being true to your commitments to yourself is very important to your self-trust and self-esteem, so take these commitments seriously.

Okay, back to explaining what happens during the arousal stage. How can you recognize when you are becoming aroused? Here are some signs that tell you that you are entering the first part of the sexual response. Not everyone will identify with everything I will list here. These are simply common patterns during arousal.

For both men and women, heart rate accelerates, muscle tension increases, and skin might begin to blush. For women, the clitoris may begin to enlarge,[3] breasts may swell, the vaginal opening may widen, and the vagina may produce lubrication. Vaginal lubrication is clear and somewhat sticky, and is produced by the Bartholin's glands (located at the mouth of the vagina) as the vagina is preparing for the entrance of the penis. Without this or some other sort of lubrication and vaginal dilation, penile penetration would be painful. Speaking of lubrication, at some point in this phase males may notice a small amount of clear, sticky fluid come from the urethra at the tip of their penis. This is called preejaculate and is produced by the bulbo-urethral glands. One purpose of preejaculate is to help lubricate the penis for vaginal penetration. Another purpose is to help neutralize the acidity of the vaginal canal so that sperm can survive on their journey to the uterus.

Women will have varied experiences during the arousal phase of the sexual response. For example, some women struggle to become aroused enough to produce vaginal lubrication. Other women become extremely aroused without ever feeling lubricated. And some women will notice lubrication but don't want penetration or don't feel emotionally prepared for it (this is called arousal non-concordance). All of these experiences are normal and can be addressed with good information.

During arousal, blood flow to the genitals generally increases. The purpose of this is to increase the amount of sensitivity to genital areas (if the process of making babies didn't feel good, people might not do it as much!) and to prepare the male and female body for orgasm. For women, the clitoris engorges with this increased blood flow (the clitoris is a mostly internal structure, so this is happening below the surface), and the glans clitoris (external) may come out from under the clitoral hood. For men, blood flow to the penis generally increases. When this happens, erectile tissue in the penis fills with blood, causing it to stiffen. This is referred to as an erection.[4] If the male did not have an erection, it would be difficult for him to enter the female's vagina (no babies). And if the female did not have an engorged clitoris, she might not enjoy sex enough to allow penetration (no babies).

It's essential to note that this list of experiences is not comprehensive, and many people have unique experiences to the ones I listed. Most people will experience varying levels of arousal during this stage (one partner might feel more desire or arousal than the other) and many will find that the trajectory through excitement is not a straight vertical line (arousal may come and go). This is normal, too!

Generally, if people continue doing the things that got them aroused initially, arousal will continue to increase in intensity. This means that as you become more aroused, your heart rate continues to increase, breathing becomes faster, blood pressure rises, and muscle tension increases for both sexes. Some individuals may experience spasms of the feet, hands, or face. With more heightened arousal, males' testes generally withdraw into the scrotum. For females, the glans clitoris generally becomes especially sensitive and retracts under the clitoral hood, the inner two-thirds of the vagina fully extend to form a "tenting" effect to create an area to receive the semen, and the outer third of the vagina becomes especially engorged with blood and turns a darker color. All of this happens typically without women recognizing it.

As I mentioned before, the journey through

arousal can vary, and the level of arousal may wax and wane during this stage. This does not mean that orgasm can't be achieved or that pleasure isn't being experienced. Our bodies have an incredible potential for sexual and emotional pleasure, and sexual experiences may vary depending on our context.

Once sufficient arousal carries you through this stage, your body is then prepared for orgasm. I want to spend a bit more time exploring orgasm in our next letter, so I'm going to take a break here.

Bonnie, knowing this first stage of the human sexual response is also an important step in making decisions before marriage that will help you maintain your goals. Decide on your goals and boundaries, then communicate them to your partner.

And also make sure that you communicate your limits in a way that he can understand. When you start dating your future husband, you tell him that you "don't want to kiss him for a long time." What you meant by that was that you didn't want to make out for long periods of time. But he interpreted this to mean that you didn't want to kiss him *yet*. After some days of confusion on both ends, you finally ask him "are you ever going to kiss me?" You are both grateful for the ensuing clarification.;)

I also want you to come back to this letter and the next one before getting married, and even afterwards. Read it with your future husband so that you both understand how your bodies experience arousal. This will make sex sweeter and help you to feel more confident and connected to each other. It will help you to be a more mature lover. It might even inspire you to be more creative!

Love,

Me

ᑌour Sexual Response Part 2

AGE 17

Dear Bonnie,

I want to provide more clarity in this letter as I talk to you about the last two stages of the sexual response—orgasm and resolution.

Like I mentioned in my previous letter, a ton of emphasis (too much in my opinion) is placed on orgasm. People normally talk about it as the most important part, best part, and end goal of sex. Ironically, placing so much emphasis on orgasm can lead to enjoying sex less and can create a lot of unnecessary pressure on sexual encounters (I'll talk more about this pressure in a few years—in letter 9). So let's talk about orgasm, but also remember that it's not the most important part!

Orgasm is the second stage of the sexual re-sponse cycle, following arousal. Also referred to as "climax," orgasm can be thought of as the peak of arousal. You get "higher" as you get more aroused and eventually you reach a "maximum height" where your body starts to respond differently than how it had during the arousal stage. That difference, that arrival at the peak, is the climax or orgasm. During orgasm, women and men may experience a sudden release of muscle tension, accompanied by involuntary muscle contractions (in the genital area, but also in other areas of the body), increased heart rate and blood pressure, heavy breathing, and perspi-ration. In addition to the pleasurable physical sen-sations, an intensely pleasant psychological feeling occurs as lots of happy hormones (oxytocin, pro-lactin, and endorphins) are released into the brain. Oxytocin is one of the hormones that is released during orgasm that helps us feel bonded and more trusting of our partners.

Surprisingly, both sexes experience many of the same sensations during orgasm. In fact, one study found that both sexes repeatedly described orgasm as "waves of pleasure through my body" and found no distinguishable differences between male and female descriptions of orgasms.[1] Men and women's orgasms, however, occur uniquely and serve slightly different purposes.

For men, orgasm consists of two stages: emission and expulsion. During emission, muscular contractions in the genital area create a buildup of semen at the base of the penis. During expulsion, the semen is released and exits through the hole at the tip of the penis (the urethra) as surrounding muscles continue to contract.

Males normally experience more intense sensations during the first couple contractions and less sensation during the following ones. The intensity of male orgasm appears to be related to the amount of semen expelled, and some men say that waiting longer between having sex results in more powerful orgasms. The function of the male orgasm, besides the experience of pleasure and bonding to his sexual partner, is to expel semen from the body that will have the potential to fertilize a female egg and make a baby.

During female orgasm, the pelvic muscles surrounding the vagina contract several times. The length of each contraction can vary, but commonly contractions last around a second each. Women report a wide range of intensities and sensations during orgasm, including how many contractions are experienced, the location of the contractions, and overall pleasure experienced. The main functions of the female orgasm are to promote procreation and to provide pleasure.[2] To me, this serves as strong evidence that God wants women to be creators, and to enjoy the process!

Once an orgasm (or sometimes more than one for women—yes, I'm serious!) occurs, the resolution stage follows. In this final part of the sexual response cycle, the body returns to its normal, pre-excitement state. Many couples will notice that this stage is marked by increased feelings of closeness, intimacy, and relaxation. Some refer to this happy state as "the afterglow."

During resolution, generally the male's penis will return to its unerect, normal size, and he will notice a decrease in sexual desire (this is often referred to as the refractory period). Each refractory period can vary in intensity and duration; some men will be able to regain an erection soon after resolution, while other men will be unable to gain an erection for multiple days. This is influenced by multiple factors including age, stress, and emotional state, among others. The female's body does not generally experience such a marked change during resolution. However, with time, her body will return to its pre-excitement state as well.

Bonnie, isn't it wonderful that God has made our bodies to not only create new life, but to also feel so strongly connected to our partners and to experience immense pleasure? A lot of people feel like this pleasure is forbidden or a sign of a loss of control. I hope that you can reframe this, and instead view this pleasure as something that God has created in us to promote our joy and happiness. I hope that you can see sex in this way—in this Godly way. It might feel confusing to you because people don't really talk about sex like this that often. Start trying to think about it. It will help you.

Love,

Me

LETTER 8

What Kind of Sex
Do You Want?

AGE 18

Dear Bonnie,

What kind of sex do you want?

If you are not deliberate about the kind of sexual relationship you want to develop with your future spouse, you will probably buy into what the world deems as "good sex." Ironically, what media often portrays as "good sex" is unsupported in any quality scientific research on fulfilling sexual relationships. In order to learn what real "good sex" is, you have to be purposeful about unlearning what the world has taught you about sex.

Let's talk about some of these mainstream messages so you can be empowered to reject them. You may recognize these messages below and you may have unconsciously accepted them. Read this list *slowly*, and ask yourself how much you believe each one.

- The goal of sex is to have an orgasm
- Sex is about performing for or pleasing the male partner
- Women must look a certain way to please their male partners
- If a man is "good enough" at sex, his female partner will always want sex with him
- Men and women experience pleasure similarly; what is pleasurable for him is always pleasurable for her
- There is always a better sexual experience out there
- We can't control our sexual impulses and often sex "just happens" because our sexual impulses were too strong
- Our sexual impulses are naughty or uninnocent
- Good sex must include a hard erection and vaginal penetration

- Good sex creates maximum physical pleasure for one or both partners
- Good sex is completely separate from trying to conceive a baby
- In order to be good at sex you must develop your sexual technique through multiple sexual experiences
- Having multiple sexual partners is better than having just one
- Only very attractive / beautiful people with certain body types or abilities can have good sex
- Those who are sexually inexperienced are immature and are "behind" the rest of their peers

Do any of these messages feel familiar? I'm guessing they do. Despite how common they are, all of these messages miss the mark. They're twisted. I hope this letter can help you unlearn these false, albeit common, portrayals of intimacy and sex. And in the process, I want to teach you what things actually contribute to thriving sexual relationships (i.e., "good sex").

First, it's essential to recognize that sexual relationships thrive when they are treated multidimensionally. Sex is not simply a physical or spiritual or emotional connection. In its optimal expression, sex encompasses all of these aspects. When all of these elements are present, couples feel closer and happier. Some of my friends at BYU have called this multidimensional experience "sexual wholeness."[1] When sex happens and only one element is present, or one is missing, sexual fragmentation occurs.[2]

I've found that religious people often experience spiritual fragmentation in their sexual relationships. Spiritual fragmentation can happen when one believes that physical pleasure is not supposed to be a part of a marital sexual relationship or when physical pleasure is ignored or avoided. Sometimes, those experiencing spiritual fragmentation feel as if their sexual urges or desires are undignified or ungodly, and should be ignored or rejected. In this case, partners may feel guilty for feeling sexual pleasure, and are left feeling confused after an encounter that felt physically pleasing but in which they experienced a spiritual conflict or felt emotionally absent. Other times, partners may struggle to physically become aroused or achieve orgasm during sexual encounters, and this repeated disappointment may lead to an apathy toward the physical element of their sexual relationship.[3]

Some people will never struggle with spiritual fragmentation, but overemphasize the physical aspects of sex. This is called physical fragmentation. This happens when the emotional and spiritual aspects are absent from a sexual experience, and one or both partners are focused solely on the physical aspects of sex. Physical fragmentation is the main characteristic of casual hook-ups or other non-committed sexual encounters. But I've also seen this happen in committed relationships when partners become consumed with their own physical appearance or their partner's, focusing only on achieving orgasm during a sexual encounter, or believing (and acting) as if sex is a performance. Physical fragmentation also occurs when there is a lack of emotional and spiritual connection between partners, for example when partners are uncommitted or when there is emotional conflict between the couple. Physical fragmentation often goes unnoticed in the beginning of a relationship, but becomes very apparent and problematic for long-term, mature relationships.

Bonnie, there have been times in dating relationships when you've used physical outlets (kissing, cuddling, general physical affection) to compensate for a lack of emotional connection. I've seen you use it when you've been confused about how you feel about a certain partner, or when you feel a bit insecure with your partner. You almost feel like if you can connect physically with them, that somehow the anxiety that you feel in the relationship will go away. I know this isn't on purpose and you don't feel like you are using your partners, but it is important to know that this is fragmentation, too. And I promise you, Bonnie, that if you aren't feeling connected to a boyfriend before kissing him, and you happen to feel momentarily more connected to him after kissing him, in the long run, this is not going to help you get where you want to be. It will leave you feeling even more confused, and you will know that you've done something that was incongruent. It's similar with sex—if you are not connected emotionally or relationally while connecting physically, you'll notice that something is off. At the same time, it is important to recognize that after marriage, if you are connecting emotionally and relationally but not sexually, you'll feel the same imbalance.

Not surprisingly, there is a ton of research that supports the truth that sex is most fulfilling when it is treated as a multidimensional experience. The findings of my favorite study on optimal sexuality are summed up here:

> The . . . findings paint a radically different picture of optimal sexuality than what is portrayed in the mass media. Popular culture sources promote achieving great sex through "secret" techniques, novelty and variety, suggesting that one is to look outside of oneself to find great sex. In contrast with these sources and mechanistic models of sex therapy, the participants in this study found techniques and sex "acts" mostly irrelevant. "Great sex" had very little to do with proper physiological functioning (e.g., hard erections, vaginal lubrication, intercourse, orgasm). The actual sexual behaviours and acts performed are far less important than the mindset and intent of the person or couple engaged in these acts.[4]

This study and multiple others support that, more than achieving orgasm, having developed technique, or having a perfect physical physique, great sex is characterized by certain mental and relationship patterns. These include valuing your own sexuality and the sexual relationship with your partner, knowing that sex is good, being present in the moment, genuinely caring for your partner, being committed to your partner, employing clear communication and deep empathy, being authentic and genuine, and viewing sex as an ongoing process of learning and exploration.[5] With these findings, it becomes clear that "great sex flourishes in relationships that deepen with maturity."[6]

Did you notice that none of these studies mentioned "mind-blowing orgasms" or "perfect sexual technique" were necessary for great sex? If you didn't notice it before, take a second to acknowledge that now. I hope it takes the pressure off of having to look a certain way, know certain techniques, or to have substantial experience before starting a sexual relationship with your spouse.[7]

I hope you feel empowered to discern between the lies the world tells about sex and what will actually enable you to have a fulfilling sexual relationship with your spouse. I hope you feel inspired to be deliberate about rejecting and unlearning the harmful sexual scripts that surround you and to replace them with your own truth.[8] Most of all, I hope that all of this is evidence of how wonderful life is, and how many tools God has given us to truly enjoy our mortal experience.

Love,

Me

Your Unique Sexuality

AGE 20

Dear Bonnie,

I wanted to focus an entire letter to you on women's sexuality because I've seen how many problems arise when women aren't treated as sexual beings, whether by their partners, or themselves. I don't want you to go through these problems. I don't want you to feel like your husband's sexuality eclipses your own. I want you to understand yourself! And I want your husband to understand you, too.

First, let's talk about your lady parts. (You'll find diagrams at the end of this letter so you can visualize what we talk about here.) Many women don't understand their own anatomy because it's a bit hard to see or understand unless they have been very purposeful about looking at themselves using a mirror (or are extremely flexible) and have been able to look at an anatomical chart as a reference point (there's a lot going on down there). So let's set some things straight.

What is commonly referred to as "the vagina" is actually the vulva. In other words, the vulva means the external genitals, made up of the mons pubis (the fleshy, hair-covered area over the pelvic bone), labia (*lay-bee-uh*) majora (outer lips of the vulva), labia minora (inner lips of the vulva), clitoris (*kli-tur-us*) (described below), and vaginal opening. The vagina is the muscular, hollow, tunnel-like structure of the female internal genitalia that connects the external genitals to the cervix. The vagina is where babies emerge during childbirth, where blood escapes during menstruation, and where the penis goes during penetration. The clitoris is a *mostly internal* sexual organ extending from the uppermost part of the labia minora to the vaginal opening. The glans clitoris, the nub-like structure at the top of the vulva is covered by the clitoral hood. This nub and its hood are the only external part of the clitoris. So what you can see is just the "tip of the iceberg," as ninety percent of the clitoris is internal.[1]

While current media emphasizes that the clitoris' only function is to provide pleasure, new research shows that the clitoris is actually a multi-tasker![2] Research on the clitoris is relatively new, and still developing, but we do know that it is both a key to sexual pleasure *and* is essential in promoting fertilization. The clitoris possesses a ton of nerve endings (It's actually made of the same stuff as penises. Fascinating, right?). Consequently, the clitoris is associated with feelings of pleasure during sexual stimulation. Clitoral stimulation also triggers the vagina to neutralize its pH, increases blood flow in the vagina, and lifts the position of the cervix, all to promote survival of sperm and maximize the chances of fertilization. Bonnie, this information points to a cool fact—the more pleasure you feel during sex, the more your body will create the conditions to create life.[3] Understanding the dual purposes of procreation and pleasure is important because many women ignore the reproductive benefits of prioritizing pleasure![4]

Bonnie, your vulva, clitoris, and other sexual organs are *incredible*. The more you learn about them and experience their power, the more you will love them. You are fed many lies about your sexual parts. For example, that vulvas are unattractive in their natural state, and need to be stained, waxed, and perfumed in order to be acceptable. Or, that the only attractive breasts are those belonging to perky and well-endowed eighteen-year-olds. Or that fertility is a burden, that periods are a nuisance, and a woman is at the height of her sexual attractiveness when she is still a teenager. Can you see how immature these beliefs are? Your body is too powerful to be evaluated in these ways.

Bonnie, your sexuality is naturally intuitive. It's as if you have a built-in "sexual wholeness" meter; you instinctively know that rewarding sexual experiences rarely happen unless the emotional and spiritual parts of the relationship are already in place. This can help you avoid incongruent sexual behavior. But sometimes, even when these pieces are in place, you may find that you lack sexual interest. This is normal.[5] Many women have a lower biological urge to be sexual for release of sexual tension compared to men, and in committed, long-term relationships, some women experience spontaneous sexual interest and arousal less frequently than their partners. So what do you do about this? What do you do with your amazing sexual potential that manifests itself only occasionally? How do you harness the power of your feminine sexuality?

First, you need to recognize your sexual inhibitors. The bad news is that there are a lot, and they will change over time. The good news is that they are easy to recognize and you can change them!

Bonnie, your biggest inhibitor is feeling impure or unfeminine when you have sexual feelings, thoughts, or fantasies. This shouldn't be a surprise to you. Many women (including you) tend to associate sexual feelings and acts with being impure or unchaste. Religious people often subscribe to the belief that women are somehow inherently more pure and righteous than men, and these concepts of purity and righteousness are closely associated with chastity. At this point in your life, you know of very few women who unabashedly love their own sexuality and being sexual with their spouse. Changing your mindset from sex being naughty and unfeminine to being good and wholesome will be a mental hurdle for you. I hope that my previous letters, especially those that talk about the good-ness of sex and how women are created in the im-age of the Divine Feminine, can also help with this paradigm shift.

Another powerful inhibitor for many women is the belief that the first priority in a sexual relation-ship is to please their partner. Consequently, you're inclined to see your own pleasure as secondary, and your own sexual desires may never be known or met. Someday, you will have to be purposeful about making your sexual pleasure and arousal just as important as your partner's. Many women don't invest in making their sexual experiences a top priority because it requires time, exploration, and risk. But as you become accepting of your sexual responses[6] and spend ample time on foreplay while your partner demonstrates patience and present-ness, without a need to "rush to the end," you will find more sexual satisfaction.[7]

Stress might be the most common inhibitor that you experience. Many women find that as their lives become more complicated, whether because of work, children, or added complexity in their relationships, spontaneous desire comes less frequently.[8] Many women that I've worked with say that they often feel inhibited by fatigue or by a long mental to-do list that is difficult to shut out when they are being sexual with their spouse.[9] A lot of times, this stress can cause her to be mentally absent during sex. "Did I change the laundry? . . . Call the babysitter? . . . Pay our phone bill? . . . Shower this week?!" Stress tends to melt away as women become more aroused, but getting to that point is sometimes a challenge. Practicing mindfulness is a wonderful way to deal with this stress. (p.s. When you get the chance to study mindfulness with a Buddhist monk in southern Spain, Do. Not. Hesitate.)

In my work as a therapist, I've found that women who have trouble getting aroused experience a lot of stress and pressure to speed through arousal to orgasm. Paradoxically, those feelings of stress about needing to experience arousal / orgasm are a barrier to women feeling aroused. Generally, *couples who have the best sex don't focus on getting anywhere*. I'm going to say that again: The couples who have the best sexual experiences don't have goal-oriented sex. Instead, they simply focus on the present moment without judgment and feeling intimately connected to one another.

Now, I've worked with so many women who feel positive about sex, make their own experience a priority, manage their stress, and try to be "in the moment" who simply don't experience sexual desire like they want to. What can you do if you find you just don't *want* sex, even when things seem to be in place?

Lots of research has shown that for many women, feeling sexual desire (excitement, arousal, eroticism) starts simply with her decision to be open to a sexual experience. I have found in my work as a therapist that sexual interest often occurs after you make a deliberate choice to create a sexual experience with your partner.[10,11,12] It may sound simple, but when you purposefully decide that you will allow yourself to mentally and physically let go—to let yourself become aroused, to be sexual with your partner, and him with you, you can find satisfying and complete sexual excitement.[13] These findings point to a central truth about female sexuality: A tremendous part of female sexuality lies with mental factors.[14]

This leads me to the amazing subject of female

orgasm. Women tend to have a different journey to and through orgasm than men do, and oftentimes, how women feel and think about their orgasms manifests itself in their lived experience.

A lot of women I work with experience confusion related to orgasm. Their concerns range from, "Have I ever orgasmed? I can't tell!" to "I can't orgasm, and I don't know why." About thirty to fourty-six percent of women say that they always or almost always orgasm when making love.[15,16] Around six percent of women will report never being able to experience orgasm.[17] Some studies have found that it takes women a significant amount of time (even years) after their first sexual experiences in order to learn how to orgasm.[18] But there is extremely good news if you find yourself in this boat: Although it may be challenging to reach or know if you have reached orgasm, research shows that your orgasmic potential (including the ability to experience and recognize an orgasm and have more pleasurable orgasms) increases with age, with a peak in orgasmic experience around the age of forty. So, Bonnie, good things lie ahead! And more good news—women are more likely than men to be multiorgasmic (meaning experiencing more than one orgasm during a sexual encounter), and women's orgasms usually last longer than men's. Not that this is a competition. . . .

What can help women learn to experience orgasm? First and foremost, women tend to be more orgasmic if they feel they have the power to make sexual choices and if they place more personal importance on having an orgasmic experience.[19] In other words, it has to be a priority, and you need to feel like an equal partner in your sexual relationship. Women who feel more confident in their sexuality and communication are more likely to orgasm. [20,21] This means relationship factors play a huge role in a woman being able to orgasm. First off, sexual experience with a steady partner (in a happy relationship) is positively associated with the frequency of having orgasms.[22] The sexual timing of the male partner also has a lot to do with the woman's ability to orgasm. Ideally, the male partner progresses slowly and concentrates on his female partner's pleasure first. Then, once she reaches climax, it's his turn. [23] I can't emphasize this last point enough: In a happy, equal sexual re-lationship—*she goes first, then him*! Similarly, cou-ples who spend more time on foreplay, and whose love-making lasts a *minimum* of fifteen minutes, find that the female partner is more likely to or-gasm.[24,25] Greater build-up of sexual desire prior to orgasm creates more pleasure for both partners. And like I mentioned before, the mental factors of being able to completely concentrate on sex and to let go of a mental to-do list contribute to being able to orgasm.[26,27] Also, women who take more of an active role during sex (e.g., woman-on-top posi-tion or using several positions) is associated with women experiencing orgasm.[28]

Do you remember when I wrote to you about my client who was shocked to find that it was possi-ble to reach orgasm while making out? In that let-ter I explained how she didn't understand her own patterns of arousal. But it wasn't just the patterns she misunderstood. It was also the mechanics of female arousal. She (and many other women, too) thought that women should orgasm during inter-course in part because she believed that the vagina is the homolog to the penis. The logic goes like this: If penile-vaginal penetration is the time for a man to orgasm, then it also must be the time that females orgasm as well. While that would be simple and pretty, and you could tie it up with a bow, that normally isn't the way it happens. In fact, less than half of women regularly experience orgasm during penetration.[29] The path to female orgasm nearly always includes clitoral stimulation, and thus the clitoris, not the vagina, is the homolog to the penis.

This clitoral stimulation happens in various ways. If you will think a few paragraphs back where I explained the anatomy of the clitoris, you'll remember that the glans clitoris (the nub) is only the tip of the iceberg of the organ of the clitoris. The rest of the clitoris (which, again, is packed with nerve endings and is made of erectile tissue that swells with blood during arousal) reaches internally, wrapping around the urethra and the vaginal column. This means that the clitoris can be stimulated both externally (on the glans clitoris, labia majora, and labia minora) and internally (from the vagina). It is likely that women who orgasm during penetration experience clitoral stimulation through the walls of the vagina or at the glans clitoris.[30] Partners have to experiment with how to stimulate the clitoris during intercourse, because many sexual positions actually leave the clitoris unstimulated. Many couples in my work find the coital alignment technique (man-on-top), and the reverse coital alignment technique (woman-on-top) helpful for stimulating the glans clitoris during penetration. Both versions of this technique involve partners changing the position of their body (if the man is on top, he moves so that the base of his penis is against the glans clitoris, partners may need to tilt their pelvises in certain ways, etc.) and intensity of pressure (partners may need to focus more or less weight on the pelvic region) as to focus on providing the glans clitoris the stimulation it needs (and deserves!). Some women won't experience orgasm with penetration, and enjoy clitorial stimulation in other ways. Exploration and practice are absolutely key in understanding your sexuality. Let yourself and your husband enjoy the journey!

Bonnie, there is so much more to understand

and explore about your own sexuality. Be purposeful about giving your sexuality as much room as your husband's sexuality when you get married. In finding this balance, you will experience more harmony and connection with him. Remind yourself frequently of the divinity and goodness of sexuality. God wants you to become and to create.

Love,

Me

Vulva

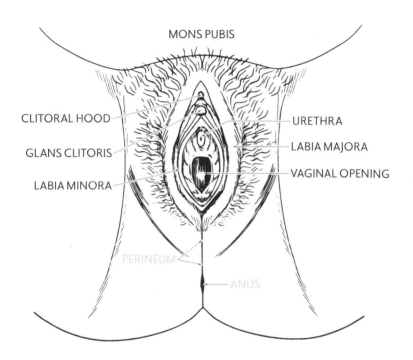

MONS PUBIS

CLITORAL HOOD

GLANS CLITORIS

LABIA MINORA

URETHRA

LABIA MAJORA

VAGINAL OPENING

PERINEUM

ANUS

Clitoris

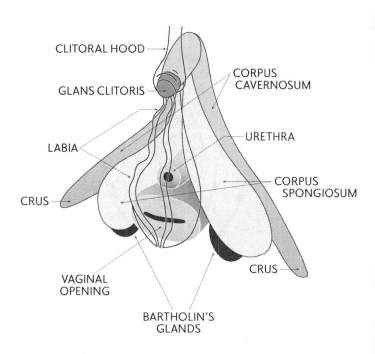

CLITORAL HOOD

GLANS CLITORIS

LABIA

CRUS

VAGINAL
OPENING

BARTHOLIN'S
GLANDS

CORPUS
CAVERNOSUM

URETHRA

CORPUS
SPONGIOSUM

CRUS

Clitoris & Penis

Parallel Structures

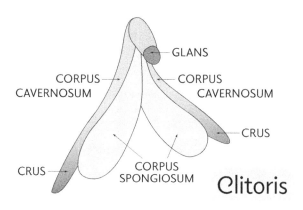

GLANS

CORPUS CAVERNOSUM

CORPUS CAVERNOSUM

CRUS

CRUS

CORPUS SPONGIOSUM

Clitoris

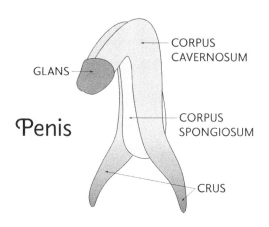

CORPUS CAVERNOSUM

GLANS

CORPUS SPONGIOSUM

Penis

CRUS

Read This Now and Before Your Honeymoon

AGE 22

Dear Bonnie,

Someday you'll get married. And you'll marry the most wonderful young man. Ironically, you've known this young man for a while. He didn't make the best first impression, but apparently that doesn't matter to you because you will love him with all of your heart. He will believe in you and love you all the way. You will trust him immensely. There will be many parts of your relationship that will grow and change over the years. One of the things that you are most looking forward to together is beginning your sexual relationship.

In fact, you find that you and your fiancé will talk about what your sexual relationship will be like once you're married. It's wonderful to be educated about sex! Appropriately learn about your body and his body, but also know that there is truly no way you can become totally prepared before marriage and this learning will continue over your entire relationship. I'm glad that you will feel so comfortable talking to him about sex—this comfort will lead to more natural and respectful communication as you navigate your sexual relationship in the future. Just make sure not to become preoccupied with the physical aspects of the sexual relationship, and make sure that you're understanding the importance of the emotional and spiritual aspects as well. If those are in place, the physical aspects of your sexual relationship will come in time.

I want to address some common misconceptions about newlywed sex.

One common belief that I've seen working with young engaged and married couples is that the law of chastity ends on your wedding night. This is false. This belief will set you up for disappointment and pain. You see, the discipline required to abstain from sex before marriage is the same discipline required when your spouse is unavailable or uninterested in sex, or, in a sexual encounter, has different speeds of arousal than you. The discipline that is necessary in controlling your thoughts, especially about others, is just as relevant (if not more) once you are married, because now you have a partner to be loyal to and honest with. The discipline you develop to respond to your own arousal before marriage will serve you in marriage. You can use that same discipline to pace your own arousal with that of your spouse (sex with only one aroused spouse is not very fun). The law of chastity doesn't end on your wedding night. While its application will vary at different times of your life, the foundational principles of respect, discipline, and temperance will be just as relevant from when you're 12 until you're 112.

You've also been told that there is a lot to fear about the first time having sex as a woman. You've heard some stuff about bleeding, about "tearing the hymen," and you've been told that it's really normal for sex to be painful. Bonnie, all of that is untrue! There should be no bleeding. There should be no pain. And your hymen doesn't "break like some rubber seal."[1] Sex should never be painful. If there is enough foreplay before penetration, most female bodies will respond with vaginal dilation and lubrication that will allow for the penis to enter without discomfort. If penetration is painful, then that is a big red light to tell you that it's either time to slow down or stop. Most importantly, remember that sex is not about a finish line!

While you will be excited to explore each others' sexuality and want each other to experience pleasure, remember that you do not *owe* your husband penetration. There are cases when women will experience painful penetration, regardless of how aroused she is, but these are the exception and not the rule. In these cases, couples should consider the different ways that they can be sexually connected besides penetration and seek professional help from a sex therapist, pelvic floor therapist, or other specialist.

One thing that surprises a lot of people as they become sexual with a partner is that a man's erection may come and go during sex. Men often have the mistaken understanding that once they become aroused, they will maintain an erection until they experience orgasm. This is not true. In fact, a man may gain and lose an erection multiple times during each sexual encounter.[2] In my professional experience, it can actually be a *good* sign that a man's erection comes and goes during the excitement phase because it means that he is spending time focusing on her pleasure.

This is important for both male and female partners to understand. Many female partners have mistaken her male partner's fluctuating erections to mean that he does not find her attractive or that he is bored with the encounter. I once worked with a newly married man who lost an erection during a sexual encounter with his wife, and her reaction to this made him so nervous that he found it difficult to gain another erection. Had she known that this was very normal for men of all ages (even young, healthy, newly-married men), she could have avoided creating that barrier in their relationship.

You've probably had some other expectations set up about first-time sex—what it will feel like, look like, or how it will end. Your first time and first days and weeks and months of having sex are discovery. You've heard about how much fun sex can be, and it's true that sex can be very fun. But most couples find that developing a really enjoyable sexual relationship together happens over time.[3] There's a learning curve. For example, most women take time to learn how to experience orgasm.[4] Some couples find that penile-vaginal intercourse on the first try doesn't work like they'd expected. Many men have to learn how to avoid orgasming too quickly (so as to not leave their partners behind!). And even after you learn and grow together and figure those things out, every sexual experience you have will be different and unique. Let your first sexual experiences be something that you create together. Don't hold yourselves to expectations you've created based on others' experiences or others' definitions of sex. It's okay to seek out resources or ask for help when things don't go the way you expect them to. But also recognize that building a happy, healthy sexual relationship is a process that simply requires time, and no matter how much research you do, you can't speed past the clock. Be careful about who you share sexual information with. Make sure that you and your husband agree about who you are sharing this information with. You need to keep very safe boundaries around your sexual relationship and you need to decide those boundaries together.

Even though you might find sex to be a bit frustrating or unnatural at first, you'll probably be pretty excited about being close to your husband in this way, and you'll want to be intimate together. Most newlyweds will make love a lot, though it isn't this way for everyone in the beginning. Over time, this frequency will diminish a bit. Most couples will eventually find that they begin to disagree a bit about how much they want to have sex. Again, this isn't a sign about incompatibility or that the marriage is going south. It's completely normal. It's just a sign that you need to talk about it. Talk about it with your sweet husband gently and kindly. He wants to be close to you.

So, Bonnie, if you feel nervous or hesitant or afraid or any combination of these emotions for your first sexual experience, take a deep breath and realize that honeymoon sex is the first step in a long journey of sexual becoming that will last your entire life. It is a beautiful journey!

Love,

Me

Your Sexual Journey

AGE 26

Dear Bonnie,

In some of my previous letters (letters 6 and 7) I wrote about the sexual response cycle. The information in those letters is absolutely essential and will be relevant for many parts of your relationship with your spouse. But I'd be setting you up for some big surprises if I didn't tell you about when sex doesn't go like that. Personal preference, ability, age, health, mental health, and energy levels are just some of the things that will influence what a couple's sexual relationship will look like.

Now don't get me wrong here. This letter is not a downer. Rather, I hope it can reflect how dynamic life is, and how you and your partner will need to trust and love and depend on each other in each stage you go through. You'd get bored if the honeymoon stage lasted forever. (It would kind of be like living your freshman year of college over, and over, and over again.)

So, let's talk about aging. Sex is just one of the many things that is influenced by the changes that accompany the maturation process. Media seldom puts value on sexuality among a population other than spry twenty-year-olds. I'm not saying that they should (I really don't think the media should play such a prominent role in our sex education in the first place), but I'm pointing out that it's just not there. So, consequently, lots of people assume that older people just don't have sex, or that sex among older folks is boring or unsexy or gross or undignified. There can't be anything further from the truth!

It's true that generally with age, spontaneous sexual desire decreases and the sexual response changes. People start noticing this generally around their mid forties to fifties. Women may find that the sensations that occur during the excitement phase wane a bit (less engorgement, less lubrication, etc.) and that the intensity of their orgasms decreases. Around the age of fifty most women will go through menopause and find that this new stage brings new symptoms like weight gain, moodiness, and vaginal dryness.[1] Men may find they desire sex less often and that it may be more difficult to gain and maintain an erection. Further, aging often brings with it health complications and illness, which can negatively influence sexual desire and functioning. These impediments are often the only things that get acknowledged when it comes to sex and aging.

What is less often recognized, however, and is reason for *great* celebration, is that age (normally) brings maturity. As couples age together or begin new relationships later in life, they have the opportunity to develop a more mature style of lovemaking that is less focused on intercourse and orgasm and more focused on intimacy. In my previous letter about what makes sex great, you'll remember that focusing on foreplay and intimacy actually adds more to sexual satisfaction than intercourse and orgasm. Let me say that again: *spending more time on foreplay and intimacy will improve your sexual relationship more than intercourse and orgasm.* The longer you know your partner and the more experienced you are at being a loving and caring spouse, the better your sex can be!

Like age, disability can also influence sexual relationships. Individuals who have impediments such as paralysis, amputation, or other physical irregularities may often feel excluded from having a "normal" sex life. An important truth here is that just because such a sexual relationship might look different from what a couple has where a disability isn't present doesn't mean that it's "less than." Couples working with a disability often can experience a freedom from sexual scripts that able-bodied couples are hindered by, as their sexual interactions may necesitate creating alternative erogenous zones (when there is no longer sensation in the genitals or other areas) and focusing less on the typical sequence of penetration and orgasm.

And then there are babies. Ironically, the natural outcomes of sex (i.e., pregnancy, childbirth, sleepless nights, insane toddlers, rebellious teenagers, etc.) are often the biggest disruption to a couple's sexual relationship. Women go through *so many changes* over the course of conception, pregnancy, and after delivery. Most women know something about these changes, but a lot of men are totally thrown for a loop when they realize the impact of childbearing and parenting on their sexual relationship with their spouse. Bonnie, this part is *especially* relevant for you, so pay attention.

Often, when a couple is trying to conceive and has been for a while—especially when there is stress around trying to get pregnant, such as grief from previous miscarriages, failed attempts at pregnancy, or other forms of infertility—sex can feel very unsexy, and well, stressful. Both partners can experience this stress in multiple ways, including lower sexual desire, difficulty in becoming aroused, difficulty gaining or maintaining erection (for men), and difficulty reaching orgasm. I worked with one couple that was desperately trying to become pregnant. The wife was on a drug that would help her to ovulate and the couple was given a week window where they had to have sex either every day or every other day. Both partners found it stressful and had trouble becoming aroused enough to experience intercourse and orgasm.

During pregnancy, your body is going to change. A lot. What was once easy for you sexaully may feel much different during pregnancy. Women may gain weight and have to deal with a changing body that they may not feel confident or sexy in. Further, women have a growing belly which will make previous sexual positions impossible or less enjoyable than before. Nausea and illness may impede a pregnant woman from desiring sex, especially for the first trimester when many women find "morning sickness" to be the strongest. Many pregnant women (especially those who suffer from severe morning sickness) say that they can't stand the smell of their husbands during pregnancy, which, as you can imagine, makes intimacy challenging.

After giving birth (both vaginally and c-section), women are advised by medical professionals to wait at least six weeks (we're talking a month and a half, people) before engaging in intercourse in order to give herself time to heal properly. While this means no intercourse (don't put the penis . . . or anything else . . . in the vagina) for the couple, it does not mean that the couple has to abstain from any sexual touching or intimacy. In fact, experiencing non-penetrative sexual intimacy during this time is a wonderful way for spouses to remain connected and to support each other.

Once the baby is born and the vaginal area has had time to heal, many women who breastfeed express confusion at how their breasts are a tool for nourishment and bonding between her and baby, but can also be a tool for eroticism and intimacy between her and her husband. Many women I work with report simply wanting their breasts to themselves!

And finally, lots of couples find that parenting will change their sexual relationship. One of the biggest hurdles to couples sexuality is finding the time and energy to be intimate. When you are waking up multiple times per night with a young baby, and then the rest of your children are waking up at the crack of dawn and not going to bed until the end of the day, when do you and your spouse find time to relax enough to be intimate with each other?

Many spouses find that they need to schedule sex in order for it to happen. With small children (and even with older children who have busy schedules), gone are the days of spontaneous sex. Some find this un-sexy, or feel that sex should always be spontaneous (this is a script perpetuated by media). But, as a friend of mine says, "planned sex can still be sexy!" I worked with one couple that would wake up at 5am (#dedication) to have some guaranteed alone time. Deliberateness is key for busy couples with families that also want to stay connected sexually.

You've heard from some friends that sex is something that a wife can use to make her husband happy. One of your acquaintences even talked about faking the enjoyment of sex and going along with it just so she wouldn't have to worry about it for the next week. Please don't make this mistake. It hurts you and it will hurt your partner. Each sexual interaction you have leaves a mark on you individually and relationally. Your girlfriends may say that it doesn't affect them, but the reality is that this sexual interaction was dishonest, one-sided, unfair for both spouses (what husband wants to feel like his wife isn't interested in sex with him?), and it perpetuates unhealthy scripts, like sex simply being a "man's thing" and sex is purely physical. It is a signal of an unbalanced interaction that, sure, if it only happens once in twenty years of marriage it might not be the sign of a ruined relationship. But most of the time, it doesn't just happen once in twenty years. So please don't go there. If you're not in the mood to make love, communicating this in a tender and gentle way is the best way to go. And, Bonnie, your husband figured out how to not have sex for a quarter of a century, including a sexually charged adolescence. I'm confident he can figure out how to wait a few more days.

I hope some of this information will feel like you've been given a heads-up when things don't go as smoothly as you're told they should. And when obstacles come up, your efforts to reconnect with your spouse will create feelings of unity that don't come when sex is easy. So don't be afraid of these stages and don't dread them. The future holds many beautiful things for you and your husband, Bonnie.

Love,
Me

SexEducated

AGE 28

Dear Bonnie,

I feel so much reverence right now. Educating you about sex is an incredibly important task. As you read this letter, you're *very* pregnant with your second child. He's a boy! And from what you know of him so far (his kicks, his movements, his hiccups), he is delightful. You'll nearly give birth to him in a taxi, and then you'll name him McKay. You're also a mother to an energetic and creative two-year-old who makes you laugh every day (and sometimes cry). Her name is Marie Nora. The love that you feel for your children and husband is more powerful than you. While you have many parts— interests, goals, and talents—you are coming to realize that the part of you that's most impactful in your process of "becoming" is that of being a creator, and that sex is an essential part of this.

This is a new idea for you. You used to see sex as something that simply *needed* to be a part of life. After all, without sex, you wouldn't exist. No people = no plan of happiness. But over time you've learned that sex's purposes both include and reach beyond procreation. And it all comes back to this truth: Sex is an incredible catalyst for development.

In order to develop, you first have to exist (i.e., you must be created). And two people (your earthly creators, or parents) must come together to create you. Sex is the ultimate creative act that God has allowed us to experience, and the potential to create life carries profound power—a power that produces "a genetically and spiritually unique being never seen before in the history of the world and never to be duplicated again in all the ages of eternity."[1] This power not only creates a new human, but also new relationships. It transforms creations (people) into creators (parents) and sexual partnerships into lifetime partnerships. The links between co-creators (parents) and children are eternal. This can never be changed, even if you wish it could.

Committing to these relationships, having a child, and being responsible for their development creates an environment very fertile for personal development. There are few if any responsibilities in life that require the constant sacrifice, dedication, and patience that marriage and parenting do. They force you to confront your weaknesses. Whether you want it or not, marriage and parenting will change you, and, if you are purposeful about it, make you a better person. And sex makes all of this possible.

Sex not only enables you to create new life, but to experience the full range of your body's power. God created your body with the potential to experience incredible pleasure. The word "pleasure" may cause some to cringe—many associate pleasure with hedonism or sin. But God created us to experience joy,[2] and part of joy is experiencing the pleasures that come with having a mortal body, including feeling the cool crisp air on your skin, eating warm homemade bread, smelling blossoms during springtime, *and* experiencing the exciting and relaxing sensations of the sexual response. The intricate systems of our bodies are a testament to God's desire for His creations to experience pleasure. When we take another look at the commandment from God in Genesis to "be fruitful, and to multiply and replenish the earth,"[3] we might see that beyond the instruction to populate the earth is an invitation to be replenished by the energizing, recharging powers of sexuality between spouses. We can allow the gift of pleasure to change us as we fully embrace the goodness in our sexual response and appreciate the divine gift of a mortal—and sexual—body.

God also intended for sex to enable us to experience incredible connection. Beyond the obvious physical connection that happens during sex is the potential for sublime spiritual connection. Many people (religious and non-religious) describe some sexual experiences as sacred—not sacred in the way that you might feel during prayer or church, but more as a shift in spiritual state. Some sexual encounters can give us a taste of the divine in how they create feelings of boundarylessness, envelopment, joy, and healing.[4,5]

Sex is the way that you can give your whole self to your spouse and accept your spouse's whole self to you. It is the ultimate expression of love and union when it is done under the circumstances that God has outlined. I like how Dr. Wendy Watson Nelson describes this idea: "True marital intimacy involves the *whole soul* of each spouse—it is the uniting of the body and the spirit of the husband with the body and the spirit of his wife." In this way, sex is a symbol of how united spouses are in all areas of their lives, as they "pray, play, struggle, grow, and enjoy life together."[6]

Bonnie, sex is about reproducing and it's also about our souls. Sex is part of God's plan so you can create life as well as eternal bonds, fully experience the power of your mortal body, and transform through complete connection with another soul. I think it is because of this that Elder Jeffrey R. Holland taught that we will never be more like God than we are when we are expressing our procreative powers.[7]

This idea might seem confusing, maybe even unattainable for you. It can be really hard to appreciate your sexuality in this stage because doing so requires a lot of effort. You might even wonder *"Is this really necessary right now?"* Responding to your sexuality in virtuous ways often needs to be practiced and learned, and the truth is most people don't innately know how to do this. This practicing and learning doesn't end once you are married or once you become a parent or once kids leave the house. The changes over your whole life, including marriage, parenting, stress, and illness, all require sexual adjusting and growth. Sex is at the center of God's plan precisely *because* it requires a lifelong commitment to learning and practicing.

Bonnie, there is deep meaning and purpose in the struggle to find sexual virtue and harmony. The nature of this struggle will look different when you are twenty-eight than when you are fifty-five. When you're twenty-eight, it's challenging to control your thoughts, to avoid lust, and to not objectify yourself or others. When you're fifty-five, and you've mastered your thoughts and lust and objectification, you might find it tricky to maintain the flame of a sexual relationship that lacks the youthful spark of yesteryear. It might be easy to ignore sex altogether—and put it on the backburner. There is wisdom in all of this struggle, though.

Only through the process of balancing the physical, spiritual, and relational, can we find true sexual fulfillment. Our Heavenly Parents want sex to help us become both disciplined and expressive, tempered and erotic, embodied and merciful.

Sex changes people. I mean that in the most obvious sense—that sex alters behavior, makes men fathers and women mothers. But I also mean it in the sense that, if you allow it, sex can help you become a better person. Sex can be a catalyst for so many good things. It can help you learn about growth, personal change, and repentance. It can offer glimpses of your eternal creative potential. It can bring you sweet babies! It can refresh and energize you. It can connect you to your spouse like no other act can.

Your sexual journey will not be an easy one. You will struggle. You'll make mistakes. You'll feel incredible sorrow and frustration. And at times you'll feel numb. But because of your sexuality, you'll have the opportunity to learn about your divine nature and eternal identity. Sex allows you to participate fully in the plan of salvation, not only as a creator, but also as a partaker of the bitter sorrows and redeeming joys of being *completely* mortal. This is why Jesus came. Make sure to let Jesus into your path of learning and growth. Bonnie, this is *all* part of the plan.

I love you,
Me

Further Reading and Education

Better Sex Through Mindfulness by Lori Brotto
This book teaches how to apply the principles of mindfulness to sex.

Sexual Wholeness in Marriage by Dean Busby,
Jason Carroll, and Chelom Leavitt
A comprehensive exploration of the sexual whole-ness model. Written for married Latter-day Saint couples.

A Better Way to Teach Kids about Sex by Jason S. Carroll,
Chelom Leavitt, Dean M. Busby, Laura M. Padilla-Walker
A scientifically informed Latter-day Saint perspec-tive on how to teach children about bodies, rela-tionships, and sexual wholeness.

Online courses and podcasts by Dr. Jennifer Finlayson-Fife, www.finlayson-fife.com

In her online courses and podcasts, Dr. Finlayson-Fife offers thoughtful responses to challenges that Latter-day Saint couples face in committed sexual relationships.

Replenish: Creating Sexual Fulfillment in Marriage by Tammy Hill, LMFT

A comprehensive guide for Latter-day Saint couples desiring a fulfilling sexual relationship.

More Than A Body by Lexie and Lindsay Kite

A book that educates readers about body image resilience, empowering them to transform their relationship with their bodies.

Becoming Cliterate: Why Orgasm Equality Matters—And How to Get It by Laurie Mintz, PhD

A guide to understanding female sexuality.

Come As You Are by Emily Nagoski

This book helps women embrace their individual sexuality and create healthy relationships with their bodies.

Courses by Carlie Palmer-Webb
https://thechristiansexeducator.com/
Comfortable, research-backed content and courses for singles, engaged, and married couples who share Christian values.

Mating in Captivity by Esther Perel
A book that addresses the sexual challenges that commonly arise in long-term, committed relationships.

Slow Sex by Diana Richardson
A step-by-step guide for couples to avoid negative sexual patterns and create intimacy that is focused on intimacy.

Intimacy & Desire: Awaken The Passion In Your Relationship by David Schnarch
This book explores why couples in long-term relationships encounter problems with sexual desire and offers steps on how to address conflict and reconnect.

Notes

LETTER 1

1. Donoghue, C., Bonillas, C., Moreno, J., Cardoza, O., & Cheung, M. (2017). Young people's perceptions of advice about sexual risk taking. *Sex Education*, *17*(1), 73-85.; Kirby, D. B. (2008). The impact of abstinence and comprehensive sex and STD/HIV education programs on adolescent sexual behavior. *Sexuality Research and Social Policy*, *5*(3), 18-27; Kohler, P. K., Manhart, L. E., & Lafferty, W. E. (2008). Abstinence-only and comprehensive sex education and the initiation of sexual activity and teen pregnancy. *Journal of Adolescent Health*, *42*(4), 344-351.; Lindberg, L. D., & Maddow-Zimet, I. (2012). Consequences of sex education on teen and young adult sexual behaviors and outcomes. *Journal of Adolescent Health*, *51*(4), 332-338. Mueller, T. E., Gavin, L. E., & Kulkarni, A. (2008). The association between sex education and youth's engagement in sexual intercourse, age at first intercourse, and birth control use at first sex. *Journal of Adolescent Health*, *42*(1), 89-96.; Secor-Turner, M., Sieving, R. E., Eisenberg, M. E., & Skay, C. (2011).

LETTER 2

1. "We are, from birth, sensual creatures, but a lot of us feel like that's a design flaw—like something's wrong, as opposed to that being what it is to be human. How much can we really embrace that core sensuality, and how much do we shame it and try to get away from it? In a lot of Christian interpretations, there's this fear that sexuality is Satan's pathway; it's going to bring us down into debauchery and a kind of indulgence, rather than an understanding that sensuality's just a part of the human experience, and it's a way of communicating—potentially—love and desire." Finlayson-Fife, Jennifer, https://www.finlayson-fife.com/blog/post/what-do-when-you-hate-sex-podcast-transcript

2. Pratt, Parley P. *The Essential Parley P. Pratt*, Salt Lake City, Signature Books, 1990, p. 124-125.

3. Pratt, Parley P. *The Essential Parley P. Pratt*, Salt Lake City, Signature Books, 1990, p. 124-125.

4. The "natural man" referred to by King Benjamin is the *opposite* of what he explains in the end of the verse: i.e., "submissive, meek, humble, patient, full of love, willing to submit to all things."

5. We don't know from the text if Corianton and Isabel actually had sex. We know that he went "after the harlot Isabel . . ." (vs. 3), that "she did steal away the hearts of many" (vs. 4), and that he went "after the lusts of his eyes" (vs. 9), but that is all the detail we get on the situation.

6. Genesis 1:22

7. Matthew 19:5-6

8. There are many interpretations of this scripture—I'm simply describing one interpretation here.

9. Nelson, Wendy W. "Love and Marriage," Brigham

Young University, The Church of Jesus Christ of Latter-day Saints, 2017.

10. Kimball, Spencer W. quoting Billy Graham, *Ensign,* May 1974, p. 7.

11. Elder Boyd K. Packer said "The power of procreation is not an incidental part of the plan of happiness; it is the key— the very key." (Packer, Boyd K. "The Plan of Happiness," Salt Lake City, UT, The Church of Jesus Christ of Latter-day Saints, April 2015)

12. President John Taylor has explained that God has "planted" natural, sexual desire in us, that, like many other parts of our natures, needs to be tempered and consecrated to its true purpose." By "sanctifying" our sexual feelings, we learn how to channel them, how to respect them, how to honor them so that they create new life and lasting love, not lust and regret. (Taylor, John. *Gospel Kingdom*, Salt Lake City, Deseret Book Publishing, 2002, p. 61).

LETTER 3

1. Another thing that has "missed the mark" are well-intentioned yet harmful lessons at church that compare your sexuality or virginity to a flower with delicate petals. There are lots of these metaphors out there (some include cupcakes or a piece of gum). Once the flower petals had been handled (or the cupcake passed around or the gum chewed), it was no longer of value. These object lessons are wrong on multiple levels, but one of the reasons they are so harmful is because they reduce you to an object that, once "handled," has less worth.

2. Matthew 18:9 "And if thine eye offend thee, pluck it out, and cast it from thee: it is better for thee to enter into life with one eye, rather than having two eyes to be cast into

hell fire."; Matthew 5:29 "And if thy right eye offend thee, pluck it out, and cast it from thee: for it is profitable for thee that one of thy members should perish, and not that thy whole body should be cast into hell; https://web.archive.org/web/20190201035604/https://qideas.org/articles/modesty-i-dont-think-it-means-what-you-think-it-means/

3. Matthew 5:28 "But I say unto you, That whosoever looketh on a woman to lust after her hath committed adultery with her already in his heart."

LETTER 4

1. Kite, Lindsay and Lexie Kite, *More Than A Body: Your Body Is An Instrument, Not An Ornament*, Houghton Mifflin Harcourt, 2020.

LETTER 5

1. "Indeed, most tragically, it is the young woman who is most often the victim, it is the young woman who most often suffers the greater pain, it is the young woman who most often feels used and abused and terribly unclean. And for that imposed uncleanliness a man will pay, as surely as the sun sets and rivers run to the sea." (Holland, Jeffrey R. *Of Souls, Symbols, and Sacraments*. Deseret Book Company, 2001) Emphasis mine.

LETTER 6

1. Author Henry Fairlie said, "Our sexuality has been animalized, stripped of the intricacy of feeling with which hu-

man beings have endowed it, leaving us to contemplate only the act, and to fear our impotence in it. It is this animalization from which the sexual manuals cannot escape, even when they try to do so, because they are reflections of it. They might [as well] be textbooks for veterinarians." [Fairlie, Henry, *Seven Deadly Sins*, University of Notre Dame Press, p. 182]

2. William Masters and Virginia Johnson conducted some of the first studies on the sexual response cycle in the 1960s. They proposed the human sexual response as a 4-stage cycle (excitement, plateau, orgasm, and resolution). Unfortunately, they focused their work mostly on men. Rosemary Basson, Beverly Whipple, Karen Brash-McGreer, and Jane Chalmers are pioneers in understanding female sexual arousal and clitoral structure. Their work has focused on non-linear models of the sexual response (i.e., not a 4-stage process) and has incorporated the importance of emotional and relationship factors.

3. If you haven't heard of the clitoris before, worry not. I'm dedicating almost a whole letter to it ;)

4. Although I wrote that women's clitorises become "engorged," another way to say it is that they become "erect." In fact, clitorises and penises are made of similar erectile tissue, but this is less-known and culturally is not referred to as an erection.

LETTER 7

1. Vance, Ellen Belle, and Nathaniel N. Wagner. "Written descriptions of orgasm: A study of sex differences." *Archives of Sexual Behavior* 5.1 (1976): 87-98.

2. Levin, R. J. (2020). The clitoris—An appraisal of its reproductive function during the fertile years: Why was it, and

still is, overlooked in accounts of female sexual arousal. *Clinical Anatomy*, *33*(1),136-145; Stimulating the clitoris catalyzes the brain to increase vaginal blood flow to raise temperature of the vagina to promote survival of sperm and changing position of the cervix, also to promote survival of sperm.

LETTER 8

1. Busby, Dean; Carroll, Jason; & Leavitt, Chelom (2013). *Sexual Wholeness in Marriage: An LDS Perspective on Integrating Sexuality and Spirituality In Our Marriages*, Deseret Book: Salt Lake City, UT, p. 52,108-109

2. Brown, Victor L. *Human Intimacy: Illusion & Reality*. Bookcraft Pubs, 1981 ,pp. 5-6, "Sexual fragmentation occurs whenever the spiritual, physical, and emotional components of human sexuality are separated or devalued"

3. I see this happen most with women, especially those around childbearing years where hormones are fluctuating, sleep isn't happening, and the demands of family life are overwhelming. I'll talk more about that in letter 11.

4. Kleinplatz, Peggy J., A. Dana Ménard, Marie-Pierre Paquet, Nicolas Paradis, Meghan Campbell, Dino Zuccarino, and Lisa Mehak. "The components of optimal sexuality: A portrait of "great sex"." *Canadian Journal of Human Sexuality* 18, no. 1-2 (2009): 1-13.

5. Other factors predicting optimal sexuality included: **Being present, focused, and embodied.** This includes being able to "let go" and allow yourself to be completely present in the moment with your partner. It also includes being able to quiet the running commentary or to-do list in your head and allow your thoughts to be in the here-and-now; **Genuine care and commitment.** This happens when there is deep

mutual respect, caring, trust, and acceptance between partners. Mature intimacy is possible only when partners truly love and cherish each other. One participant in a personal study put it this way "any [sexual experience] without a full commitment [can't] yield full satisfaction." In other words, genuinely caring about your partner is impossible in casual sexual encounters. When partners truly care for each other, they are more likely to experience selfless intimacy, which can literally double sexual pleasure, as you get satisfaction not only from your own sexual response but from your partner's as well. This selfless approach to sex, paradoxically, is far more likely to bring sexual satisfaction to both men and women; **Extraordinary communication and heightened empathy.** The most fulfilling sex includes verbal and non-verbal communication before, during, and after sexual encounters. This type of communication is that which allows partners to be fully known and that enables partners to respond with sensitivity and care; **Authenticity, being genuine and transparent.** In contrast to the idea of sex being a performance, the most fulfilling sexual experiences are when partners can be fully themselves. In these situations, partners feel freedom to be honest and transparent with themselves and their partners about sexual likes, dislikes, or ideas. An important part of being sexually authentic is acknowledging and rejecting previous harmful scripts or beliefs about sex and replacing those with genuine likes, dislikes, and ideas; **Transcendence, bliss, peace, transformation, healing.** Many people use religious language to describe their greatest sexual experiences and emphasize the transformative, growth-enhancing and healing qualities of great sex; **Exploration, interpersonal risk-taking, fun.** Many participants likened great sex to an ongoing "discovery process" where partners are able to be creative and continuously learn more about themselves and their partners.

6. Ibid.

7. Peggy Klienplatz in Levine, Stephen B., Candace B. Risen, and Stanley E. Althof, eds. *Handbook of Clinical Sexuality for Mental Health Professionals*. Routledge, 2011. "None of the participants felt that the facility of optimal sexuality was a natural talent that had sprung fully formed in youth . . . most stated that a prerequisite for developing the capacity to experience great sex was unlearning everything they had learned about sex while growing up."

8. "Sex of this caliber does not simply happen, it must be invited into one's life. It requires deliberate planning and prioritizing. . . . All of the participants emphasized devoting time to sex." (Ibid)

LETTER 9

1. "The cultural understanding of clitoris is 'the little nub at the top of the vulva.' But like I mentioned before, the biological understanding of clitoris is more like 'far ranging mostly internal anatomical structure with a head emerging at the top of the vulva.'" (Nagoski, Emily. *Come as You Are: The Surprising New Science That Will Transform Your Sex Life*. Simon and Schuster, 2015.)

2. Levin, R. J. (2020). The clitoris—An appraisal of its reproductive function during the fertile years: Why was it, and still is, overlooked in accounts of female sexual arousal. *Clinical Anatomy*, 33(1), 136-145

3. While it's possible to get pregnant from unpleasurable (and even unwanted) sex, increasing pleasure during sex can assist in the procreative capacity of intercourse.

4. Dr. Janelle Howell, a pelvic floor specialist, argues that this understanding is important, because "If you believe your clitoris only provides pleasure in the midst of a trying to conceive season, you may be inclined to prioritize just "getting the deed done", while ignoring the other functional and reproductive benefits of prioritizing pleasure."

5. It is also common for women to be the higher desire partner. About 25% of women will have more interest and arousal than their partner, and because of the common narrative of women being less interested in sex, this sometimes makes them feel like they are misfits. The truth is that there is great variability in sexual interest among women! Leavitt, C. E., Leonhardt, N. D., Busby, D. M. & Clarke, R. W. (2020). When is enough enough?: Curvilinear associations of orgasm and relational and sexual satisfaction. *Journal of Sexual Medicine*; Leavitt, C. E., Leonhardt, N. D., & Busby, D. M. (2019). Different ways to get there: Evidence of a variable female sexual response cycle. *The Journal of Sex Research*, 56, 899-912.

6. Graham, Cynthia A., Stephanie A. Sanders, Robin R. Milhausen, and Kimberly R. McBride. "Turning on and turning off: A focus group study of the factors that affect women's sexual arousal." *Archives of Sexual Behavior* 33, no. 6 (2004): 527-538.

7. Ibid.

8. And then there are also many women who experience spontaneous desire as well! They may find that thinking about sex with their partner, or imagining certain physical, emotional, or spiritual responses make them excited to be intimate with their husband. This is also normal.

9. Kontula, Osmo, and Anneli Miettinen. "Determinants of female sexual orgasms." *Socioaffective Neuroscience & Psychology* 6, no.1 (2016): 31624.

10. Basson, Rosemary. "The female sexual response: A different model." *Journal of Sex & Marital Therapy* 26, no. 1 (2000): 51-65

11. Ibid.

12. Graham, Cynthia A., Stephanie A. Sanders, Robin R. Milhausen, and Kimberly R. McBride. "Turning on and turning off: A focus group study of the factors that affect women's sexual arousal." *Archives of Sexual Behavior* 33, no. 6 (2004): 527-538.

13. Basson, Rosemary. "The female sexual response: A different model." *Journal of Sex & Marital Therapy* 26, no. 1 (2000): 51-65.

14. I once had a professor who explained to our class that the largest sexual organ in both men and women was . . . the brain!

15. Nagoski, Emily. *Come as You Are: The Surprising New Science That Will Transform Your Sex Life*. Simon and Schuster, 2015.

16. Kontula, Osmo, and Anneli Miettinen. "Determinants of female sexual orgasms." *Socioaffective Neuroscience & Psychology* 6, no. 1 (2016): 31624.

17. Ibid.

18. Ibid., It's difficult to measure the average time of "learning to orgasm" due to variation in sexual debut, frequency of intercourse, and living situations with sexual partners, but this study showed that 40-50% of women had their first orgasm in intercourse only after the age of 20. The average age of first intercourse was 17—so half of these individuals, on average, took about 3 years to be able to orgasm during intercourse.

19. Ibid.

20. Ibid.

21. Sanchez, Diana T., Amy K. Kiefer, and Oscar Ybarra. "Sexual submissiveness in women: Costs for sexual autonomy and arousal." *Personality and Social Psychology Bulletin* 32, no. 4 (2006): 512-524: "Women with an orgasm disorder tend to behave according to the traditional female scripts, in which the woman remains passive, does not let go mentally, and waits until her male partner evokes feelings of arousal and pleasure in her."

22. Kontula, Osmo, and Anneli Miettinen. "Determinants of female sexual orgasms." *Socioaffective Neuroscience & Psychology* 6, no. 1 (2016): 31624.

23. Ibid.

24. Ibid.

25. Paterson, Laurel QP, Ellie Shuo Jin, Rhonda Amsel, and Yitzchak M. Binik. "Gender similarities and differences in sexual arousal, desire, and orgasmic pleasure in the laboratory." *The Journal of Sex Research* 51, no. 7 (2014): 801-813. "Greater build-up of sexual arousal desire prior to orgasm significantly predicted orgasmic pleasure for both genders."

26. Ibid.

27. Adam, Françoise, Marie Géonet, James Day, and Pascal De Sutter. "Mindfulness skills are associated with female orgasm?." *Sexual and Relationship Therapy* 30, no. 2 (2015): 256-267.

28. Ibid.

29. Ibid.

30. If you've ever heard someone mention the "g-spot" in the vagina, sex researchers now know that this is actually just the back of the clitoris!

LETTER 10

1. Nagoski, Emily. *Come as You Are: The Surprising New Science That Will Transform Your Sex Life*. Simon and Schuster, 2015.

2. Metz, Michael E., and Barry W. McCarthy. *Coping With Erectile Dysfunction: How to Regain Confidence and Enjoy Great Sex*. New Harbinger Publications, Incorporated, 2004.

3. Bonnie, you've probably been fed the lie that "good sex" is something that happens if you have "chemistry" with your partner. If there is no "chemistry," then you'll need to find someone else. Some people will use this reasoning to justify becoming intimate before marriage—you know, "just to make sure." I don't think you're going down that path, but I do think that you've bought into the lie that if you and your partner are a good fit, that "good sex" will happen effortlessly. Some people also use this reasoning to justify extra-marital sexual relationships. I hope you can see by now that this reasoning is faulty on multiple levels—not only because sex is so much more than physical alignment, but also because sexual relationships are something that require committed and consistent effort.

4. Kontula, Osmo, and Anneli Miettinen. "Determinants of female sexual orgasms." *Socioaffective Neuroscience & Psychology* 6, no. 1 (2016): 31624.

LETTER 11

1. Slon, S., *Sexuality in Midlife and Beyond*. Harvard Health Publications, 2005

LETTER 12

1. Elder Jeffery R. Holland says: "But I know of nothing so earth-shatteringly powerful and yet so universally and unstintingly given to us as the God-given power available in every one of us from our early teen years on to create a human body, that wonder of all wonders, a genetically and spiritually unique being never seen before in the history of the world and never to be duplicated again in all the ages of eternity—a child, *your* child—with eyes and ears and fingers and toes and a future of unspeakable grandeur." (Holland, Jeffrey R. *Of Souls, Symbols, and Sacraments*. Deseret Book Company, 2001.).

2. 2 Nephi 2:25

3. Genesis 1:28

4. "There is a sense of being transported to another place and time. . . . Boundaries between you and your partner shift or cease to exist. . . . Profound mutual caring and joy overflow the bond between you. You're moved to tears, appreciating other people past and present, and what it means to be human . . ." Schnarch, David, *Passionate Marriage*, Norton, 2009.

5. "Participants often reported a sense of timelessness during great sex or a sense of the infinite. . . . Many participants used religious language to describe their greatest sexual experiences. One participant stated, 'At this moment, we were in the presence of God' and described a feeling of being 'enveloped in this beautiful white light.' Another remarked, 'It was revelatory—an epiphany.' Many participants emphasized the transformative, growth-enhancing and healing qualities of great sex. . . . Another suggested that great sex 'can change you, can make you more than you are.'

Kleinplatz, Peggy J., A. Dana Ménard, Marie-Pierre Paquet, Nicolas Paradis, Meghan Campbell, Dino Zuccarino, and Lisa Mehak. "The components of optimal sexuality: A portrait of "great sex"." *Canadian Journal of Human Sexuality* 18, no. 1-2 (2009): 1-13.

6. Nelson, Wendy W., "Love and Marriage," Brigham Young University, The Church of Jesus Christ of Latter-day Saints, 2017. (Emphasis mine)

7. Ibid.

BONNIE YOUNG is a licensed marriage and family therapist, frequent presenter and podcast guest, and author of several academic articles on religion and mental health. She has licensure to practice therapy in Utah and Washington and specializes in treating clients with anxiety, religious OCD / scrupulosity, and sexual disorders. Bonnie holds a bachelor's degree in history with an emphasis in Latter-day Saint women's history and a master's degree in marriage and family therapy, both from BYU. Born and raised in the Seattle area, she currently lives in Logan, Utah where she is completing her doctoral studies at Utah State University in marriage and family therapy. Her dissertation will explore questions about women's experience with power dynamics in Latter-day Saint marriages.

SAM PETERSEN works in marketing at a software company based in Seattle by day. He moonlights as a dreamer and schemer with Bonnie on projects like *Sex Educated* and the online therapy clinic they co-founded. Sam grew up in beautiful Morgan, Utah. He holds a bachelor's degree in communications from BYU where he wrote an award-winning feature series on pornography for the school's newspaper in a journalism class. (This stroke of fortune would catch the positive attention of his future wife, kickstart his early career as a copywriter, and inspire his pursuit of editing these very pages.) Sam also holds an MBA from IESE Business School in Barcelona, Spain. An actor hobbyist, Sam portrayed Lemuel in the Book of Mormon Video Library.

BONNIE AND SAM are best friends and soul mates. They met in Mexico working for the church as Missionary Training Center (MTC) teachers in 2013 and were married in Seattle in 2015. After a transient period that took them through Provo, Barcelona, San Diego, and Seattle, they're happy to call Cache Valley home for a while. Together they founded Azure Counseling, an online clinic aimed at providing quality therapy for clients with ties to the Latter-day Saint tradition. In their free time you can find them playing frisbee, backpacking, and trying new restaurants. They're also the parents of two small children, a privilege that makes the aforementioned free time scarce and precious.

Made in the USA
Las Vegas, NV
10 June 2024

90944320R00085